12⁰⁰

635.9

Labadie, Emile L.
  Native plants for use in the
California landscape / Emile L.
Labadie ; with drawings by Denise
Robertson Devine. -- 1st ed. --

c.2

Sierra City, Calif. : Sierra City
Press, 1978.
  244 p. : ill. ; 23 cm.

  1. Wild flower gardening--
California.   2. Botany--California.
3. Landscape gardening--California.
4. Plants, Ornamental--California.
I. Title.

Adult Pkt        820611          820610 CRic
C000406           /KLD                   82-B2592
                                 78-565610

# Native Plants
# for use in the
# California Landscape

Placed by East Bay Municipal Utility District in the interest of promoting water conservation

EBMUD

County Map of California

# Native Plants for use in the California Landscape

Emile L. Labadie

*With drawings by*
*Denise Robertson Devine*

Sierra City Press 1978

# Table of Contents

# PREFACE

This book developed as I taught my students at Merritt College. The list of plants is purely an arbitrary one. Other native plants could well have been used.

These particular plants were discussed as we found them - in home gardens as we walked the streets of Berkeley and Oakland, in local nurseries, in parks and other civic areas, in the University of California Botanical Garden, in Tilden Botanical Garden and plants that either were purchased with meager funds or were donated by many good friends of our horticultural program.

People in the San Francisco Bay area are especially fortunate in having a wealth of plant material available to them the year around, in a relatively small geographic area.

Also available to those interested in plants, exotic as well as native, are the many educational programs offered by colleges and universities and by organizations such as the California Native Plant Society, the California Horticultural Society and so many others.

Much of the information has been gathered and compiled from the time I was active in the Scouting program and led many a trip in the outdoors, and also in the years I spent with the San Mateo County Department of Agriculture.

Pest control methods are not suggested other than to recommend an integrated program. First should be good plant management, then the use of biological controls wherever feasible; then the use of chemicals only as needed and as suggested by such people as the University of California Cooperative Extension Service. The County Departments of Agriculture should also be consulted relative to rules and regulations as to proper and safe use of pesticides.

Pests mentioned are those commonly seen in the bay area. They include both insects and diseases. Poison Oak is discussed because it is probably the most common California native plant. It should be considered a weed pest. It should be readily identified by those who are on the trail of other natives, and it should always be treated with respect.

It must be emphasized that a healthy plant may be much less susceptible to certain pests. If that plant is infested or infected, then the resultant injury may be less severe. Good plant management necessitates, of course, a knowledge of plants in the first place.

It is a pleasure to acknowledge the assistance of many people either directly or indirectly. Denise Robertson Devine's excellent illustrations reflect her expertise along those lines and I am most grateful to her. Robert Cooney was the one who did the typing and retyping, the layout and he pulled the whole thing together. His help was indispensable.

Without my students I would never have done this book. I have tried to keep at least one step ahead of them as together we progressed in learning about California native plants and others as well.

The horticultural education of my students has always been my first concern; so for them, most of all, this book has been written. Many of them are now the leading horticulturists in the state of California and sometimes beyond. They all deserve much credit for their devotion and their interest as together we developed a horticulture program with no facilities other than the great outdoors. Standard equipment for horti- culture students of mine has included boots and rain gear, the latter for the many times that we have tramped, studied and worked, in spite of some very uncomfortable weather.

To my wife Evelyn, to my four sons and two daughters, and to my students, I lovingly dedicate this book.

Emile L. Labadie

Horticultural Consultant
Emeritus Professor
Ornamental Horticulture
Merritt College

Oakland, California
June 1, 1978

# INTRODUCTION

This book is a discussion of California native plants. In any discussion, a few definitions may be in order.

Every plant is a native of some particular location. One definition of the word native is '. . . produced in a region or country . . .' The word indigenous means, according to the same source, 'originating in a place or country - native'. Thus native and indigenous apparently mean the same thing.

This book uses the term native, referring to plants that grow naturally within the state of California. Any plant that is not native is called an exotic. Therefore, any plant that is not native to the state of California is exotic. Any plant that is found only in a restricted geographical area, such as, for example, San Diego County, is endemic. *Pinus torreyana,* Torrey Pine, is endemic to San Diego County - actually to a very small part of that particular county, as well as to Santa Rosa Island.

## SUGGESTIONS FOR GROWING NATIVE PLANTS

We should grow these plants as we grow any other plants. We should create an environment for them in the landscape that is comparable to their native environment.

Some ferns for example grow in shady, moist situations. Others are seen in rocky, dry environments. People may be discouraged from growing native plants because they are not aware of their specific requirements. They could have trouble growing exotic plants for the same reason. It is important, then, to study each plant and to know the best conditions for that particular plant.

Correct moisture conditions are very important. Heavy clay soils and resultant poor drainage situations can be fatal to plants. Surface drainage alone is not sufficient. There should be good drainage in the vicinity of the root system, whether plants are growing on a slope or on a level surface.

Another common problem is that people are not aware sometimes of the devasting effect of allowing the soil to build up around the base of woody plants. As a matter of fact, these same people may even raise the soil level around the base of a valuable Coast Live Oak, then plant ferns, Azaleas, and Rhododendrons, install and use all too frequently an

8

irrigation system. Within a very short time, that choice Oak tree might be seen to decline and ultimately die. This type of thing happens all too often.

We might plant on mounds (raised areas). This is especially effective in the growing of Ceanothus and Manzanitas in the landscape. Crown Rots such as Phytophthora might be discouraged by this type of corrective action.

Some native plants may need to be irrigated, even though they might be very tolerant of dry, arid situations. A periodic irrigation during certain hot, dry periods might help to keep those plants in better condition and perhaps to make a better appearance in the landscape.

To improve drainage in heavy, clay soils, we can use organic materials of all kinds. Each time that a plant is installed in the soil, the addition of organic material such as leaf mold, sawdust, and compost to the backfill (the soil being returned to the hole) may aid in improving the drainage in a particular location. We should not, however, use an excessive amount of organic matter, otherwise this might result in a temporary loss of nitrogen. Also, it might result in too much water being held around the plant.

Fertilizers should be used with caution. Some plants look better in the landscape without being fertilized. A particular plant, for example, may be more compact if that plant is growing under conditions causing a certain amount of plant stress. Again, we should know our plants.

We can grow native plants in the landscape if we know the requirements for those specific plants. Those who design landscapes, therefore, might avail themselves of the services of knowledgeable horticulturists, if they themselves do not know their plants.

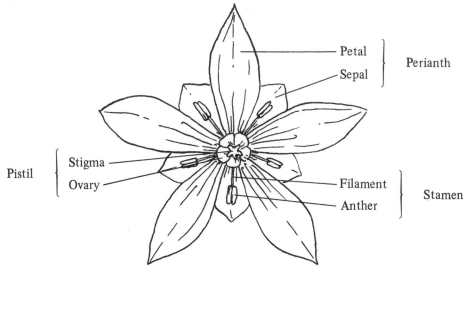

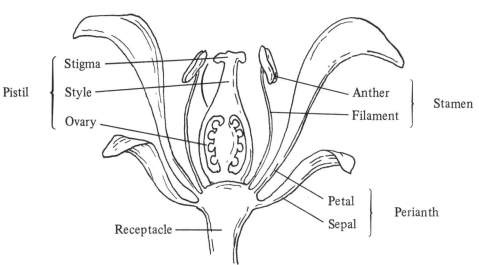

Table I. FLOWER PARTS

# BOTANICAL CHARACTERISTICS AND KEYS

The following lists are arbitrary ones. Some plants, for example, might be considered to be either trees or shrubs. Trees are usually thought to be taller than shrubs, but that is not always true. Trees are looked upon as having single trunks, but again, some trees are multi-trunked.

Some shrubs may spread out and be effective in covering a soil area. They might be used as ground covers then, even though they might be taller than most of the plants that we use as ground covers.

An example of a very variable plant is *Rhus diversiloba,* Poison Oak. This notorious plant can grow as a shrub, a vine, or even as a ground cover plant. Even though it is a most attractive plant, especially in the fall season, it is certainly not recommended for use in the landscape. It is included in this book because anyone studying native plants should be able to recognize it and know its characteristics.

The lists of plants according to characteristics are for the benefit of serious horticulture students. These listings should be helpful to them.

## TREES

Palms
  *Washingtonia filifera*

Conifers
  *Abies bracteata*
  *Abies concolor*
  *Abies magnifica*
  *Calocedrus decurrens*
  *Chamaecyparis lawsoniana*
  *Cupressus macrocarpa*
  *Pinus contorta*
  *Pinus coulteri*
  *Pinus muricata*
  *Pinus ponderosa*
  *Pinus radiata*
  *Pinus sabiniana*
  *Pinus torreyana*
  *Pseudotsuga menziesii*
  *Sequoia sempervirens*
  *Sequoiadendron giganteum*
  *Thuja plicata*
  *Tsuga heterophylla*

Broadleaf Evergreen
  *Arbutus menziesii*
  *Lithocarpus densiflora*
  *Prunus lyonii*
  *Quercus agrifolia*

11

# Table II. TYPES OF INFLORESCENCES

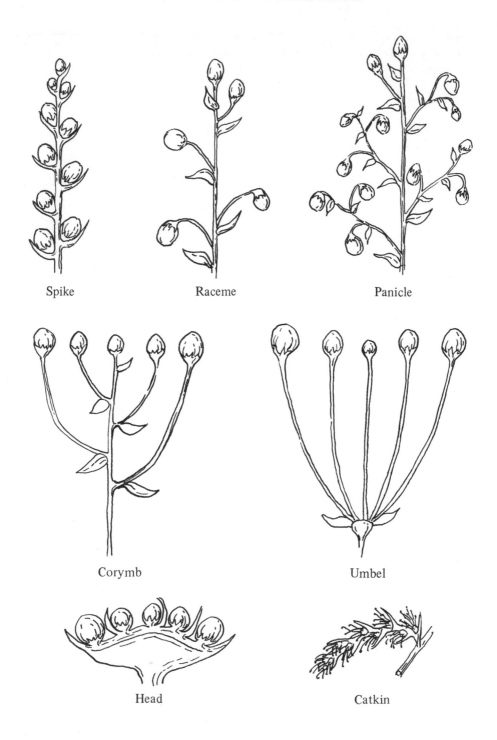

Spike

Raceme

Panicle

Corymb

Umbel

Head

Catkin

12

Lyonothamnus floribundus
  var. asplenifolius
Myrica californica
Prunus ilicifolia

Quercus chrysolepis
Quercus wislizenii
Umbellularia californica

Broadleaf Deciduous
  Acer macrophyllum
  Acer negundo var. californicum
  Aesculus californica
  Alnus oregona
  Alnus rhombifolia
  Cercocarpus betuloides var.
    traskiae

Cercocarpus ledifolius
Juglans hindsii
Platanus racemosa
Quercus douglasii
Quercus kelloggii
Quercus lobata
Sambucus caerulea

Leaves Alternate
  Alnus oregona
  Alnus rhombifolia
  Arbutus menziesii
  Cercocarpus betuloides
    var. traskiae
  Cercocarpus ledifolius
  Juglans hindsii
  Lithocarpus densiflora
  Myrica californica
  Platanus racemosa

Prunus ilicifolia
Prunus lyonii
Quercus agrifolia
Quercus chrysolepis
Quercus douglasii
Quercus kelloggii
Quercus lobata
Quercus wislizenii
Umbellularia californica

Leaves Opposite
  Acer macrophyllum
  Acer negundo var. californicum
  Aesculus californica

Lyonothamnus floribundus
  var. asplenifolius
Sambucus caerulea

Leaves Toothed
  Acer macrophyllum (or entire)
  Acer negundo (or entire)
  Aesculus californica
  Alnus oregona
  Alnus rhombifolia
  Arbutus menziesii (or entire)
  Cercocarpus betuloides
    var. traskiae
  Juglans hindsii
  Lithocarpus densiflora

Myrica californica (or entire)
Platanus racemosa (or entire)
Prunus ilicifolia
Quercus agrifolia
Quercus chrysolepis (or entire)
Quercus kelloggii
Quercus lobata
Quercus wislizenii (or entire)
Sambucus caerulea

Leaves Entire
  Arbutus menziesii (or toothed)

Platanus racemosa (or toothed)

*Cercocarpus ledifolius*
*Lyonothamnus floribundus*
  *var. asplenifolius*
*Myrica californica (or toothed)*

*Prunus lyonii*
*Quercus douglasii*
*Umbellularia californica*

Leaves Revolute
*Alnus oregona*

*Cercocarpus ledifolius*

Leaves Palmately Lobed
*Acer macrophyllum*

*Platanus racemosa*

Leaves Pinnately Lobed
*Acer negundo (terminal leaflet)*
*Alnus oregona (slightly)*
*Quercus douglasii*

*Quercus kelloggii*
*Quercus lobata*

Leaves Palmately Compound
*Aesculus californica*

Leaves Pinnately Compound
*Acer negundo*
*Juglans hindsii*

*Lyonothamnus floribundus*
  *var. asplenifolius*
*Sambucus caerulea*

Foliage Grayish
*Pinus sabiniana*

*Pinus torreyana*

Flowers Reddish
*Chamaecyparis lawsoniana (male)*

Flowers Yellowish
*Acer macrophyllum*
*Sambucus caerulea*

*Umbellularia californica*

Fruit Bluish to Purplish
*Abies bracteata*
*Abies concolor (or other)*
*Abies magnifica*
*Myrica californica*
*Prunus ilicifolia*

*Prunus lyonii*
*Sambucus caerulea*
*Umbellularia californica*
*Washingtonia filifera*

Fruit Reddish
*Arbutus menziesii*

*Calocedrus decurrens*

# KEY TO TREES

A tree can be defined as a woody plant that is at least 10 feet in height, usually has a single trunk (not always), and usually has a well-defined crown (but not always).  A tree can be narrow-leaved as with the Gymnosperms (Conifers) or it can be broadleaved as with the Angiosperms (the flowering plants).  Also, a tree can either be evergreen or deciduous.

*Gymnosperms (Conifers)*

Leaves evergreen and needle-like (Pines), awl-shaped, scale-like or linear (Firs, etc.).  Fruit is usually a cone, with seeds borne naked at the base of a scale.

Leaves needle-like and fascicled.  In bundles of 1 to 5
    A. Leaves in bundles of 2
        Leaves stout. Often twisted. Dark green. 1 to 3 inches long.
        Scales prickly.  Cones ¾ to 2½ inches long.

                                                        *Pinus contorta, p. 146*

        Leaves long and rigid. Usually twisted. Yellowish-green.
        4 to 6 inches long. Cones 2 to 3½ inches long. Roundish.
        Scales sharp-pointed.

                                                          *Pinus muricata, p. 150*

    B. Leaves in bundles of 3
        Leaves with sharp points. Stiff. Heavy. Straight. Deep
        bluish-green. 5 to 12 inches long. Cones 9 to 14 inches long.
        Scales sharp-pointed.

                                                          *Pinus coulteri, p. 148*

        Leaves glossy, yellow-green to dark green. Stiff.  In clusters
        at end of the branches.  4 to 11 inches long.  Cones 3 to 5
        inches long.  With prickly scales.

                                                          *Pinus ponderosa, p. 152*

        Leaves bright green to bluish-green. Densely crowded.
        3½ to 6 inches long. Cones asymmetrical.  2 to 5 inches long.
        Scales not sharp-pointed.

                                                          *Pinus radiata, p. 154*

        Leaves grayish-green. Stiff.  Wiry. Comparatively slender.
        7 to 13 inches long. Cones 6 to 10 inches long, with
        sharp-pointed scales.

                                                          *Pinus sabiniana, p. 156*

    C. Leaves in bundles of 5
        Leaves a dark grayish-green.  In terminal clusters.  Stiff.
        7 to 12 inches long.  Cones a chocolate-brown color.

# Table III. LEAF SHAPES

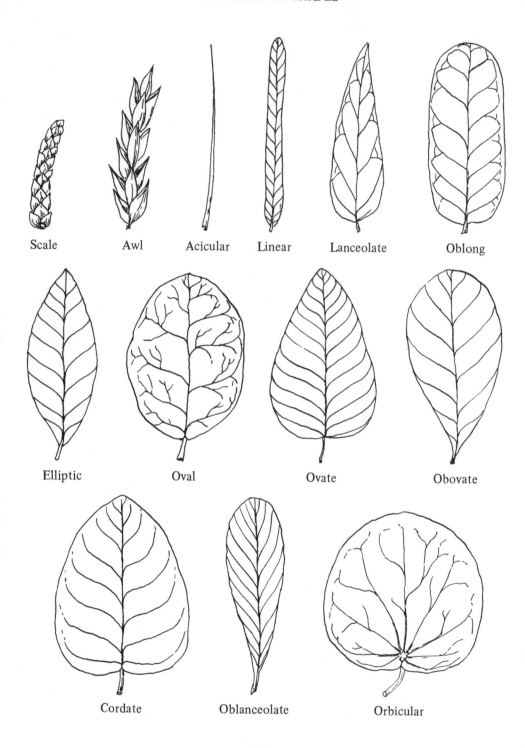

Scale     Awl     Acicular     Linear     Lanceolate     Oblong

Elliptic     Oval     Ovate     Obovate

Cordate     Oblanceolate     Orbicular

Broadly ovoid.  4 to 6 inches long.  Tips of scales triangular
at apex.

*Pinus torreyana, p. 158*

Leaves not needle-like.  Not fascicled
  A. Leaves linear
      1. Leaves sharp-pointed (to the touch)    *Abies bracteata, p. 32*
      2. Leaves not sharp-pointed
         a. Cones erect
            I. Leaf base usually twisted.  Old bark grayish
*Abies concolor, p. 34*
            II. Leaf base not twisted.  Old bark reddish
*Abies magnifica, p. 36*
         b. Cones not erect
            I. Cones with conspicuous 3-pointed bracts
            which extend beyond cone scales
*Pseudotsuga menziesii, p. 168*
            II. Cones without conspicuous 3-pointed bracts
               A. Leaves attached singly
*Tsuga heterophylla, p. 222*
               B. Leaves not attached singly
*Sequoia sempervirens, p. 214*
  B. Leaves awl-shaped         *Sequoiadendron giganteum, p. 216*
  C. Leaves scale-like
      1. Male flowers red      *Chamaecyparis lawsoniana, p. 92*
      2. Male flowers not red
         a. Branchlets forming flat sprays
            I. Leaf bases decurrent   *Calocedrus decurrens, p. 72*
            II. Leaf bases not decurrent   *Thuja plicata, p. 220*
         b. Branchlets not forming flat sprays
*Cupressus macrocarpa, p. 100*

*Angiosperms*

Broadleaf,  Deciduous
  A. Leaves compound
      1. Leaves palmately compound    *Aesculus californica, p. 46*
      2. Leaves pinnately compound
         a. Leaflets usually 3
*Acer negundo var. californicum, p. 42*
         b. Leaflets usually 5 to 9   *Sambucus caerulea, p. 210*
         c. Leaflets usually 15 to 23   *Juglans hindsii, p. 128*

B. Leaves not compound
   1. Leaves opposite
      a. Palmately lobed           *Acer macrophyllum, p. 40*
      b. Not lobed               *Cornus nuttallii, p. 96*
   2. Leaves alternate
      a. Leaves palmately lobed    *Platanus racemosa, p. 160*
      b. Leaves pinnately lobed
         I. Leaves bluish-green    *Quercus douglasii, p. 174*
         II. Leaves not bluish-green
             A. Lobes bristly-pointed
                             *Quercus kelloggii, p. 176*
             B. Lobes not bristly-pointed
                             *Quercus lobata, p. 178*
      c. Leaves not conspicuously lobed
         I. Fruit long, hairy, twisted
             A. Leaves ½ to 1 inch long
                           *Cercocarpus ledifolius, p. 90*
             B. Leaves 1½ to 2¼ inches long
                 *Cercocarpus betuloides var. traskiae, p. 88*
         II. Fruit not long, hairy, twisted
             A. Leaves revolute     *Alnus oregona, p. 48*
             B. Leaves not revolute
                           *Alnus rhombifolia, p. 50*

*Broadleaf, Evergreen*

Trees palm-like               *Washingtonia filifera, p. 228*
Trees not palm-like
  A. Leaves opposite
         *Lyonothamnus floribundus var. asplenifolius, p. 132*
  B. Leaves alternate
    1. Leaves aromatic
      a. Leaves resinous-dotted on underside
                     *Myrica californica, p. 142*
      b. Leaves not resinous-dotted below
                 *Umbellularia californica, p. 224*
    2. Leaves not aromatic
      a. Leaves entire or nearly so
         I. Fruit a reddish berry   *Arbutus menziesii, p. 54*
         II. Fruit reddish to purplish drupe
                     *Prunus lyonii, p. 166*

b. Leaves toothed
    I. Leaves with prominent parallel lateral veins
Lithocarpus densiflora, p. 130
    II. Leaves without prominent parallel lateral veins
      A. Fruit a reddish or purplish drupe
Prunus ilicifolia, p. 164
      B. Fruit an acorn
        1. Leaves glabrous both sides or nearly so
          a. Leaves often convex
Quercus agrifolia, p. 170
          b. Leaves usually flatish
Quercus wislizenii, p. 180
        2. Leaves hairy to glaucous below
Quercus chrysolepis, p. 172

## SHRUBS

**Broadleaf Evergreen**

*Adenostoma fasciculatum*
*Atriplex lentiformis var. breweri*
*Carpenteria californica*
*Ceanothus impressus*
*Comarostaphylis diversifolia*
*Dendromecon harfordii*
*Eriogonum arborescens*
*Eriogonum giganteum*
*Fremontodendron californicum*
*Fremontodendron mexicanum*
*Galvezia speciosa*
*Garrya elliptica*

*Heteromeles arbutifolia*
*Mahonia aquifolium*
*Mahonia nevinii*
*Mahonia pinnata*
*Rhamnus californica*
*Rhamnus crocea*
*Rhododendron macrophyllum*
*Rhus integrifolia*
*Rhus laurina*
*Rhus ovata*
*Ribes speciosum*
*Vaccinium ovatum*

**Broadleaf Deciduous**

*Acer circinatum*
*Amelanchier alnifolia*
*Calycanthus occidentalis*
*Cercis occidentalis*
*Cornus nuttallii*
*Corylus cornuta var. californica*

*Holodiscus discolor*
*Physocarpus capitatus*
*Rhododendron occidentale*
*Rhus diversiloba*
*Ribes sanguineum*
*Rubus parviflorus*

**Leaves Whorled, Fascicled or in Clusters**

*Adenostoma fasciculatum*
*Eriogonum arborescens*

*Galvezia speciosa (or opposite)*
*Rhamnus crocea (or alternate)*

## Table IV. LEAF TIPS

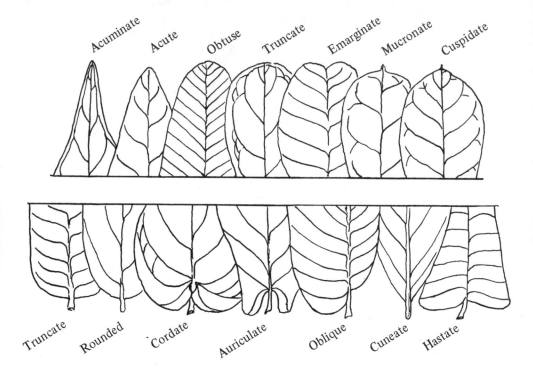

Acuminate · Acute · Obtuse · Truncate · Emarginate · Mucronate · Cuspidate

Truncate · Rounded · Cordate · Auriculate · Oblique · Cuneate · Hastate

## Table V. LEAF BASES

Leaves Alternate

*Amelanchier alnifolia*
*Atriplex lentiformis var. breweri*
*Ceanothus impressus*
*Cercis occidentalis*
*Comarostaphylis diversifolia*
*Corylus cornuta var. californica*
*Dendromecon harfordii*
*Eriogonum giganteum*
*Fremontodendron californicum*
*Fremontodendron mexicanum*
*Heteromeles arbutifolia*
*Holodiscus discolor*
*Mahonia aquifolium*
*Mahonia nevinii*

*Mahonia pinnata*
*Physocarpus capitatus*
*Rhamnus californica*
*Rhamnus crocea (or fascicled)*
*Rhododendron macrophyllum*
*Rhododendron occidentale*
*Rhus diversiloba*
*Rhus integrifolia*
*Rhus laurina*
*Rhus ovata*
*Ribes sanguineum*
*Ribes speciosum*
*Rubus parviflorus*
*Vaccinium ovatum*

## Leaves Opposite

Acer circinatum
Calycanthus occidentalis
Carpenteria californica

Cornus nuttallii
Galvezia speciosa (or whorled)
Garrya elliptica

## Leaves Toothed

Acer circinatum
Amelanchier (above middle
or entire)
Carpenteria californica (or entire)
Ceanothus impressus (appears
to be crenate)
Comarostaphylis diversifolia
Cornus nuttallii (or entire)
Corylus cornuta var. californica
Dendromecon harfordii (or entire)
Heteromeles arbutifolia
Holodiscus discolor
Mahonia aquifolium

Mahonia nevinii
Mahonia pinnata
Physocarpus capitatus
Rhamnus californica (or entire)
Rhamnus crocea
Rhus diversiloba (usually toothed)
Rhus integrifolia (or entire)
Rhus ovata (or entire)
Ribes sanguineum
Ribes speciosum (upper half)
Rubus parviflorus
Vaccinium ovatum

## Leaves Entire

Adenostoma fasciculatum
Amelanchier alnifolia (or toothed
above middle)
Atriplex lentiformis var. breweri
Calycanthus occidentalis
Carpenteria californica (or toothed)
Ceanothus impressus (appears
to be crenate)
Cercis occidentalis
Cornus nuttallii (or toothed)
Dendromecon harfordii
Eriogonum arborescens
Eriogonum giganteum

Fremontodendron californicum
Fremontodendron mexicanum
Galvezia speciosa
Garrya elliptica
Rhamnus californica (or toothed)
Rhamnus crocea
Rhododendron macrophyllum
Rhododendron occidentale
Rhus diversiloba (usually toothed)
Rhus integrifolia (or toothed)
Rhus laurina
Rhus ovata (or toothed)
Ribes speciosum (lower half)

## Leaves Revolute

Carpenteria californica
Ceanothus impressus
Comarostaphylis diversifolia

Eriogonum arborescens
Garrya elliptica
Rhamnus californica (sometimes)

## Leaves Palmately Lobed

Acer circinatum
Corylus cornuta (sometimes
3-lobed)

Fremontodendron mexicanum
(shallowly)
Physocarpus capitatus

*Fremontodendron californicum
(sometimes 3-lobed)*

*Ribes sanguineum
Ribes speciosum (sometimes)
Rubus parviflorus*

Leaves Pinnately Lobed
*Rhus diversiloba (leaflets)*

Leaves Palmately Compound
*Rhus diversiloba*

Leaves Pinnately Compound
*Mahonia aquifolium
Mahonia nevinii*

*Mahonia pinnata*

Foliage Grayish
*Atriplex lentiformis var. breweri
Dendromecon harfordii
Eriogonum arborescens*

*Eriogonum giganteum
Mahonia nevinii*

Flowers Bluish to Purplish
*Ceanothus impressus*

*Rhododendron macrophyllum (or
other)*

Flowers Pinkish
*Eriogonum arborescens (or
whitish)
Rhododendron macrophyllum
(or other)
Rhus integrifolia (or whitish)*

*Rhus ovata (or whitish)
Ribes sanguineum
Rubus parviflorus (or whitish)
Vaccinium ovatum (or whitish)*

Flowers Reddish
*Calycanthus occidentalis
Cercis occidentalis*

*Galvezia speciosa*

Flowers Yellowish
*Dendromecon harfordii
Fremontodendron californicum
Fremontodendron mexicanum
Mahonia aquifolium*

*Mahonia nevinii
Mahonia pinnata
Rhamnus crocea (yellow-green)*

Fruit Bluish to Purplish
*Amelanchier alnifolia
Garrya elliptica
Mahonia aquifolium
Mahonia nevinii*

*Mahonia pinnata
Rhamnus californica
Ribes sanguineum
Vaccinium ovatum*

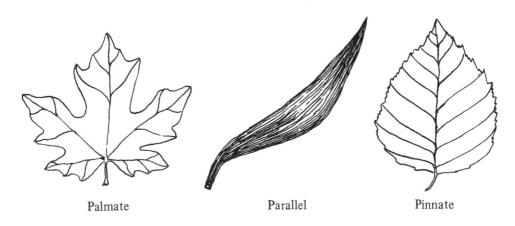

| Palmate | Parallel | Pinnate |

Table VI. VENATION

Fruit Reddish

*Acer circinatum*
*Atriplex lentiformis (or purplish)*
*Comarostaphylis diversifolia*
*Cornus nuttallii*

*Heteromeles arbutifolia*
*Rhamnus crocea*
*Rhus integrifolia*
*Rhus ovata*
*Rubus parviflorus*

Fruit Whitish

*Rhus diversiloba*

*Rhus laurina*

## KEY TO SHRUBS

A shrub is a woody plant that is usually multi-trunked. It is commonly between 3 and 10 feet in height. In this book, woody plants that are lower than 3 feet in height are said to be ground covers.

*Broadleaf, Deciduous*

Leaves compound   *Rhus diversiloba, p. 190*
Leaves not compound
  A. Leaves opposite
   1. Leaves aromatic   *Calycanthus occidentalis, p. 74*
   2. Leaves not aromatic   *Acer circinatum, p. 38*
  B. Leaves alternate
   1. Leaves lobed or at least sometimes lobed
    a. Flowers white
     I. Leaves very hairy. Very soft to the touch.
      *Rubus parviflorus, p. 206*

II. Leaves mostly glabrous.  (Mature leaves)
> *Physocarpus capitatus, p. 144*
b. Flowers pink > *Ribes sanguineum, p. 198*
c. Flowers not colorful
> *Corylus cornuta var. californica, p. 98*
2. Leaves not lobed
a. Leaves usually toothed upper half of leaf
I. Fruit bluish or purplish
> *Amelanchier alnifolia, p. 52*
II. Fruit not bluish or purplish
> *Holodiscus discolor, p. 126*
b. Leaves not toothed
I. Flowers magenta-colored.  Pea-shaped
> *Cercis occidentalis, p. 86*
II. Flowers white to pinkish.  Not pea-shaped
> *Rhododendron occidentale, p. 188*

*Broadleaf, Evergreen*

Leaves compound
A. Leaves grayish-green when mature  *Mahonia nevinii, p. 138*
B. Leaves not grayish-green
1. Leaves crowded to overlapping.  Crinkly
> *Mahonia pinnata, p. 140*
2. Leaves not crowded to overlapping
> *Mahonia aquifolium, p. 134*
Leaves not compound
A. Leaves fascicled or whorled
1. Leaves grayish.  White-hairy below
> *Eriogonum arborescens, p. 106*
2. Leaves not grayish
a. Leaves linear  *Adenostoma fasciculatum, p. 44*
b. Leaves not linear  *Rhamnus crocea, p. 184*
B. Leaves opposite
1. Flowers red  *Galvezia speciosa, p. 118*
2. Flowers white  *Carpenteria californica, p. 76*
3. Flowers not as above  *Garrya elliptica, p. 120*
C. Leaves alternate
1. Leaves lobed or at least sometimes lobed
a. Flowers red  *Ribes speciosum, p. 200*

b. Flowers lemon-yellow. Flowering all at one time
*Fremontodendron californicum, p. 114*
c. Flowers orange-yellow. Prolonged flowering
*Fremontodendron mexicanum, p. 116*
2. Leaves not lobed
  a. Leaves toothed or at least sometimes toothed
    I. Leaves grayish    *Dendromecon harfordii, p. 102*
    II. Leaves not grayish
      A. Flowers bluish
*Ceanothus impressus, p. 82*
      B. Flowers not bluish
        1. Bell-shaped flowers. Flowers white or pink
          a. Fruit red at maturity
*Comarostaphylis diversifolia, p. 94*
          b. Fruit black at maturity
*Vaccinium ovatum, p. 226*
        2. Flowers not bell-shaped
          a. Fruit black at maturity
*Rhamnus californica, p. 182*
          b. Fruit not black at maturity
            I. Leaves commonly boat-shaped
*Rhus ovata, p. 196*
            II. Leaves not boat-shaped
              a. Leaves irregularly toothed,
              Ovate to nearly orbicular
*Rhus integrifolia, p. 192*
              b. Leaves regularly toothed
*Heteromeles arbutifolia, p. 124*
  b. Leaves entire
    I. Leaves grayish
      A. Flowers grayish and in clusters to 12 inches
      across.    *Eriogonum giganteum, p. 110*
      B. Flowers greenish and in small clusters
*Atriplex lentiformis var. breweri, p. 68*
    II. Leaves not grayish
      A. Leaves boat-shaped. Fruit a white drupe
*Rhus laurina, p. 194*
      B. Leaves not boat-shaped
*Rhododendron macrophyllum, p. 186*

# Table VII. LEAF MARGINS

Entire      Serrate      Double Serrate

Dentate      Sinuate      Crenate      Revolute

Palmately Lobed      Pinnately Lobed

# GROUND COVERS

Broadleaf Evergreen
*Arctostaphylos densiflora*
*Arctostaphylos edmundsii*
*Arctostaphylos hookeri*
*Arctostaphylos uva-ursi*
*Artemisia pycnocephala*
*Asarum caudatum*
*Baccharis pilularis*
*Ceanothus gloriosus*
*Ceanothus griseus*
  *var. horizontalis*
*Ceanothus purpureus*

*Equisetum hyemale*
*Eriogonum fasciculatum*
*Fragaria chiloensis*
*Gaultheria shallon*
*Mahonia nervosa*
*Polystichum munitum*
*Ribes viburnifolium*
*Salvia leucophylla*
*Satureja douglasii*
*Woodwardia fimbriata*
*Zauschneria californica*

Broadleaf Deciduous
*Romneya coulteri*

*Symphoricarpos albus*

Leaves Alternate
*Arctostaphylos densiflora*
*Arctostaphylos edmundsii*
*Arctostaphylos hookeri*
*Arctostaphylos uva-ursi*
*Artemisia pycnocephala*
*Asarum caudatum*
*Baccharis pilularis*

*Ceanothus griseus*
  *var. horizontalis*
*Gaultheria shallon*
*Mahonia nervosa*
*Ribes viburnifolium*
*Romneya coulteri*
*Zauschneria californica*

Leaves Opposite
*Ceanothus gloriosus*
*Ceanothus purpureus*
*Salvia leucophylla*

*Satureja douglasii*
*Symphoricarpos albus*

Leaves Whorled, Fascicled or in Clusters
*Eriogonum fasciculatum*

Leaves Toothed
*Baccharis pilularis (or entire)*
*Ceanothus gloriosus*
*Ceanothus griseus var. horizontalis*
*Ceanothus purpureus*
*Fragaria chiloensis*
*Gaultheria shallon*

*Mahonia nervosa*
*Ribes viburnifolium (or entire)*
*Romneya coulteri*
*Salvia leucophylla*
*Satureja douglasii*
*Zauschneria californica (or entire)*

Leaves Entire
*Arctostaphylos densiflora*

*Baccharis pilularis (or toothed)*

*Arctostaphylos edmundsii*
*Arctostaphylos hookeri*
*Arctostaphylos uva-ursi*
*Artemisia pycnocephala*
*Asarum caudatum*

*Eriogonum fasciculatum*
*Ribes viburnifolium (or toothed)*
*Symphoricarpos albus*
*Zauschneria californica (or toothed)*

Leaves Revolute
*Ceanothus griseus var. horizontalis*    *Eriogonum fasciculatum*

Leaves Palmately Lobed
*Ribes viburnifolium (sometimes)*    *Symphoricarpos albus (sometimes)*

Leaves Pinnately Lobed
*Artemisia pycnocephala (linear lobes)*    *Romneya coulteri (nearly compound)*

Leaves Palmately Compound
*Fragaria chiloensis*

Leaves Pinnately Compound
*Mahonia nervosa*

Grayish Foliage
*Artemisia pycnocephala*
*Eriogonum fasciculatum*
*Romneya coulteri*

*Salvia leucophylla*
*Symphoricarpos albus*
*Zauschneria californica*

Flowers Bluish to Purplish
*Ceanothus gloriosus*
*Ceanothus griseus var. horizontalis*

*Ceanothus purpureus*
*Salvia leucophylla*

Flowers Pinkish
*Arctostaphylos densiflora (or whitish)*
*Arctostaphylos edmundsii*
*Arctostaphylos hookeri (or whitish)*
*Arctostaphylos uva-ursi (or whitish)*

*Eriogonum fasciculatum (or whitish)*
*Gaultheri shallon (or whitish)*
*Ribes viburnifolium*
*Symphoricarpos albus (or whitish)*

Flowers Reddish
*Zauschneria californica*

Flowers Yellowish
*Baccharis pilularis (male)*    *Mahonia nervosa*

Fruit Bluish to Purplish

*Ceanothus griseus var. horizontalis*    *Mahonia nervosa*
*Gaultheria shallon*

Fruit Reddish

*Arctostaphylos densiflora*        *Arctostaphylos uva-ursi*
*Arctostaphylos edmundsii*         *Fragaria chiloensis*
*Arctostaphylos hookeri*           *Ribes viburnifolium*

Fruit Whitish

*Symphoricarpos albus*


## KEY TO GROUND COVERS

A ground cover is a plant that can either be herbaceous or woody. Herbaceous plants have no persistent woody stems. The plants in this category are up to 3 feet in height usually, and sometimes taller than that.

Plants *herbaceous* - usually having no persistent woody stems.

A. Fern-like
    Fronds pinnate. 2 to 5 feet long.    *Polystichum munitum, p. 162*
    Fronds bi-pinnate. to 10 feet long.    *Woodwardia fimbriata, p. 230*
B. Not fern-like
    1. Rush-like. With perennial stems. Spreading by rhizomes.
                        *Equisetum hyemale, p. 104*
    2. Not rush-like.
        a. Leaves aromatic
            Aroma strongly mint-like    *Satureja douglasii, p. 212*
            Aroma not strongly mint-like    *Asarum caudatum, p. 66*
        b. Leaves not aromatic
            I. Leaves compound    *Fragaria chiloensis, p. 112*
            II. Leaves not compound
                  *Zauschneria californica, p. 232*

Plants *not herbaceous* - having persistent woody stems.

A. Leaves compound    *Mahonia nervosa, p. 136*
B. Leaves not compound
    1. Leaves whorled usually    *Eriogonum fasciculatum, p. 108*
    2. Leaves not whorled
        a. Leaves opposite

Table VIII. TYPES OF LEAVES

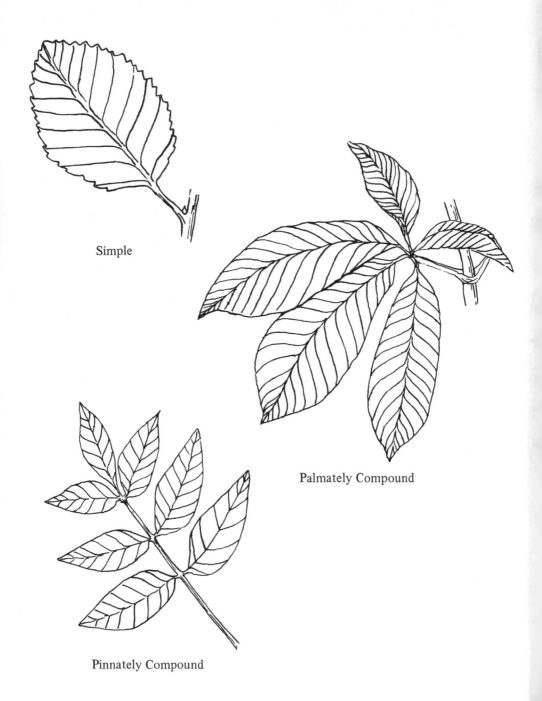

Simple

Palmately Compound

Pinnately Compound

I. Leaves entire or lobed

*Symphoricarpos albus, p. 218*

II. Leaves toothed

    A. Leaves grayish    *Salvia leucophylla, p. 208*

    B. Leaves not grayish

        1. Plant height 4 to 20 inches or more

*Ceanothus gloriosus, p. 78*

        2. Plant height 2 to 4 feet

*Ceanothus purpureus, p. 84*

b. Leaves alternate

I. Leaves toothed or sometimes toothed.

    A. Leaves aromatic    *Ribes viburnifolium, p. 202*

    B. Leaves not aromatic

        1. Flowers bluish

*Ceanothus griseus var. horizontalis, p. 80*

        2. Flowers not bluish

            a. Flowers to 9 inches across

*Romneya coulteri, p. 204*

            b. Flowers not to 9 inches across

                I. Flowers bell-like

*Gaultheria shallon, p. 122*

                II. Flowers not bell-like

*Baccharis pilularis, p. 70*

II. Leaves entire and lobed

*Artemisia pycnocephala, p. 64*

III. Leaves entire and not lobed

    A. Stomata on both sides of leaves

        1. Branches blackish

*Arctostaphylos densiflora, p. 56*

        2. Branches reddish-brown

*Arctostaphylos hookeri, p. 60*

    B. No stomata on upper surface of leaves

        1. Fruit bright red berries. Old branches shreddy.

*Arctostaphylos uva-ursi, p. 62*

        2. Fruit reddish-brown berries. Branches not shreddy.

*Arctostaphylos edmundsii, p. 58*

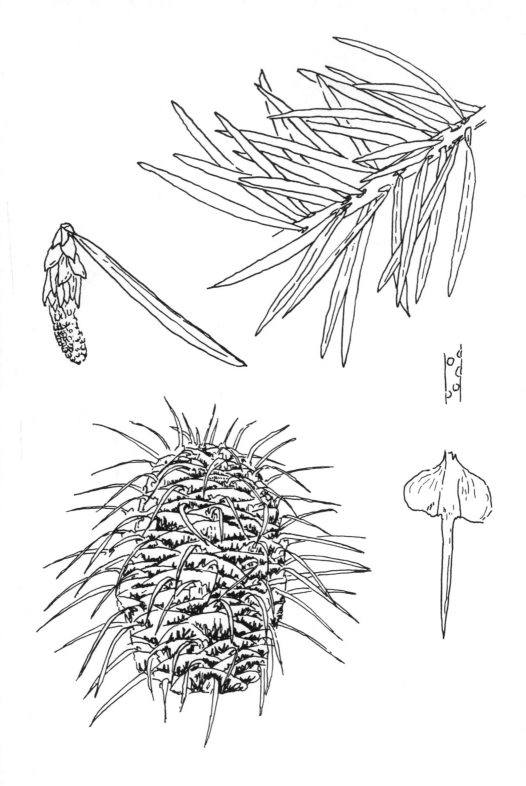

32

# Abies bracteata

**Common Name**  Santa Lucia Fir, Bristlecone Fir

**Family**  Pinaceae

**Leaves**  Evergreen, stiff, sharp-pointed, glabrous. Nearly flat above. Not grooved. With 2 broad white bands and a prominent midrib below. 1¼ to 2¼ inches long. Linear.

**Flowers**  Male catkins yellow

**Fruit**  Bristly cones from 2½ to 4 inches long. Cones are purplish-brown with bristly spines ½ to 2 inches long. Erect.

**Environment**  Rocky slopes and canyons from 2000 to 4500 feet. Full sun. Cool coastal area.

**Pests**  Aphids

**Propagation**  Seed, cuttings. Stratify seed 3 to 4 months.

**Rate of Growth**  Slow to moderate

**Pruning**  Not necessary

**Seasonal Value**  Foliage, cones

**Shape**  Pyramidal, with pendulous branches nearly to ground.

**Spread**  15 to 20 feet; Diameter from ½ to 2½ feet

**Height**  30 to 100 feet

**Soil**  Rocky, dry, acid

**Use**  Specimen, hedge

**Origin**  Santa Lucia Mountains of Monterey County, California

**Comments**  A beautiful formal tree in the landscape. Bark of older trees is slightly fissured and branches are somewhat pendulous at the ends.

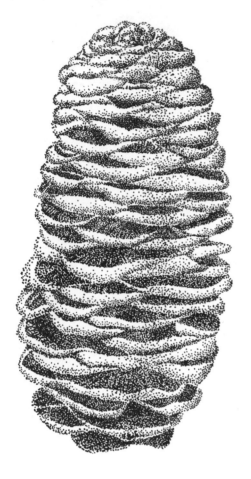

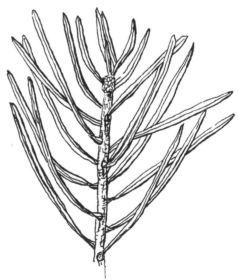

# Abies concolor

**Common Name**  White Fir, Silver Fir

**Family**  Pinaceae

**Leaves**  Evergreen. Vary in young trees from yellowish-green to bluish-green. Turning whitish with age. Short, stiff, bluntly-pointed. ¾ to 2½ inches long. Linear. Stomata on both surfaces. Base usually twisted.

**Flowers**  Usually May or June. Reddish.

**Fruit**  Purplish cones, or olive-green or dark yellowish-green. Cylindrical. 2 to 5½ inches long. Ripen in September or October. Erect.

**Environment**  Grows best in cold areas. Most are from 4000 to 7000 feet in California. Will grow from 2000 to 11,000 feet in California and Oregon.

**Pests**  Dwarf Mistletoe, various moths, beetles

**Propagation**  Seed, cuttings. Stratify seed 1½ months.

**Rate of Growth**  Moderate to slow

**Pruning**  Not necessary

**Seasonal Value**  Foliage, cones

**Shape**  Pyramidal

**Spread**  40 to 60 feet; diameter from 3½ to 6 feet

**Height**  60 to 100 (200) feet

**Soil**  Best in a deep, rich, moist light loam, but tolerant to coarse, and dry. Needs good drainage. Has a deep root system.

**Use**  Specimen, lumber

**Origin**  Rocky Mountains and Pacific Coast regions from New Mexico and Colorado west to Oregon and California. (See below.)

**Comments**  Wood is soft, fine-textured, straight-grained, nearly white. Is not aromatic. Easy to work. Used for paper pulp, general building construction purposes, boxes, doors, crates, etc. Most important commercial fir in the United States. Old bark grayish. In California, in the mountains of San Diego County, north through the Sierra Nevada and North Coast Ranges to Del Norte, Modoc and Siskiyou Counties.

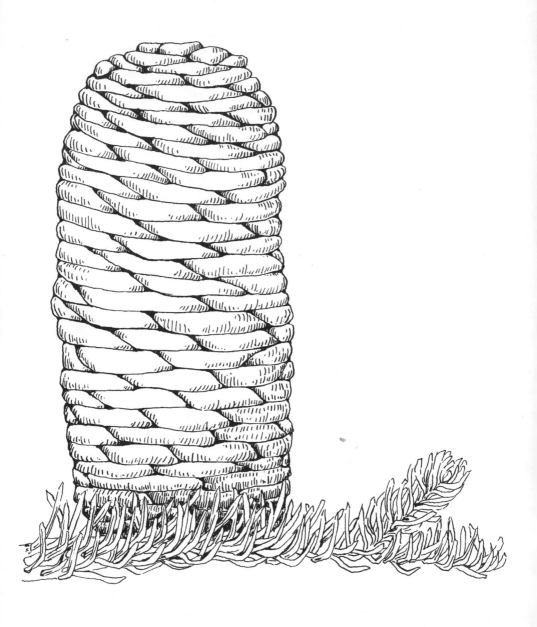

# Abies magnifica

**Common Name**  Red Fir, California Red Fir, Silver Tip

**Family**  Pinaceae

**Leaves**  Evergreen. On upper branches they curve upwards, on lower they are two-ranked. Base not twisted. Entire at tip. Usually 4-angled. Glaucous at first then becoming bluish-green. With whitish stomatal bands on all surfaces. ¾ to 1½ inches long. Linear.

**Flowers**  Male: dark reddish purple; Female: Short, rounded and scale-like. Pale green.

**Fruit**  Deep-purple cones when mature. Often tinged with brown. From 5 to 8 inches long. Bracts hidden by the scales. Seed is dispersed in September and October. Medium to low viability. Cones erect.

**Environment**  From 5000 to 9000 feet. Where the winters are long and with a heavy snowpack and short summers. Temperature range from 25 to 80 degrees. Not too tolerant to shade.

**Pests**  Dwarf Mistletoe, Fir Engraver, Fir Borer (Flatheaded and Round-headed), Heart Rots.

**Propagation**  Seed, cuttings. Stratify seed 1½ months.

**Rate of Growth**  Slow

**Pruning**  Not necessary

**Seasonal Value**  Foliage, cones

**Shape**  Pyramidal, with a round top

**Spread**  Diameter 2½ to 4 feet

**Height**  60 to 200 feet

**Soil**  In the Sierras of California, does best on glacial moraines or on other areas with deep soils. pH varies from about 5.0 to 6.0. Moist, but well-drained. Most of moisture during the winter.

**Use**  Specimen. Used for Christmas trees.

**Origin**  Canada, Nevada, Oregon, Washington, northwest California south to the Kern River. In Coast Ranges from Oregon to Lake County.

**Comments**  Wood is soft but firm, rather brittle. Straight and usually fine-grained. More durable than any of the other native firs. Has deeply furrowed dark red bark, hence the name Red Fir. The short branches droop except at the top of the tree, where they turn upwards. Top is brittle and often breaks. On young trees, the bark is smooth and whitish.

# Acer circinatum

**Common Name**  Vine Maple

**Family**  Aceraceae

**Leaves**  Deciduous, opposite. Thin, glabrous. Palmately 5 to 11 lobed. Round to cordate in outline, with sharp teeth. Reddish when immature, turning a dull dark green above. Brilliantly red and orange in the fall. 2 to 7 inches across. Same length.

**Flowers**  Minute. With reddish or purple sepals and greenish-white petals. In drooping clusters (corymbs) in April and May. Monoecious.

**Fruit**  Double samara. Glabrous. Red. Nearly straight out. 1½ inches long. Persisting until the following spring. June to October.

**Environment**  Coastal mountains of the Pacific Coast. In moist woods, along stream banks. From 1000 to 5000 feet. Best in partial shade. Tolerant to heat and cold.

**Pests**  Aphids, Verticillium Wilt, Mildew

**Propagation**  Seed, cuttings. Stratify seed for 2 months.

**Rate of Growth**  Moderate

**Pruning**  To control and to shape

**Seasonal Value**  Foliage, flowers, fruit, fall color

**Shape**  Multi-trunked. Small tree or shrub which is often vine-like in habit.

**Spread**  25 to 35 feet; Diameter 8 to 10 inches

**Height**  25 to 35 feet

**Soil**  Tolerant. Best in rich, moist soil. Deep roots.

**Use**  Specimen. Tubs. Firewood when dead.

**Origin**  Pacific Coast of the United States and Canada. Down through Humbolt County in California. Also to Butte and Yuba Counties.

**Comments**  Best not to prune after growth starts in the spring, because of excessive bleeding. Bark is usually thin, grayish-brown, tinged with red.

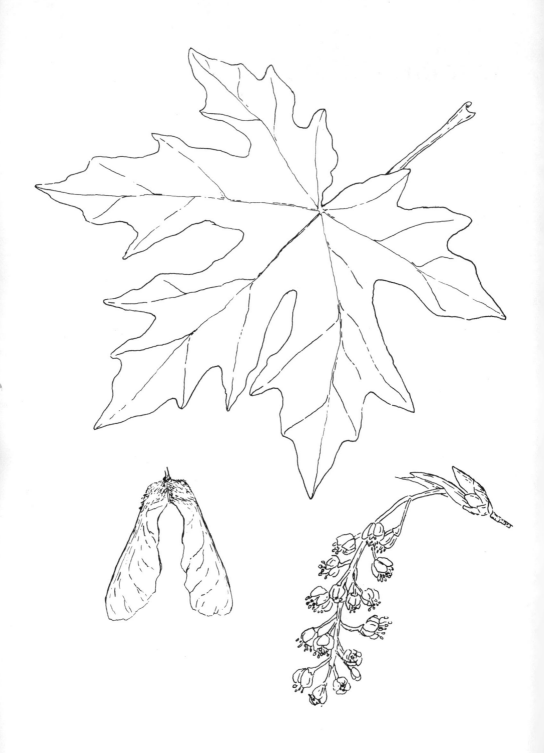

# Acer macrophyllum

**Common Name**  Bigleaf Maple

**Family**  Aceraceae

**Leaves**  Deciduous. Opposite. Deeply palmately five-lobed. Blue-green. Petioles 6 to 12 inches long. Leaves glabrous. Turning reddish-yellow in the fall. Largest leaves of any native American Maple. 6 to 12 inches long and about as wide.

**Flowers**  Yellowish. Fragrant. In drooping racemes. After the leaves in the spring. April to May. Monoecious.

**Fruit**  Double or sometimes triple samara. Green at first, then turning brownish. Maturing from August to October. From 1¾ to 2 inches.

**Environment**  Grows along stream banks, moist canyons. Tolerant to considerable shade when young. Best if has light near top at least. In California to about 5500 feet.

**Pests**  Aphids, various caterpillars, Verticillium Wilt.

**Propagation**  Seed, cuttings. Stratify seed for 2 months.

**Rate of Growth**  Moderate to rapid

**Pruning**  Little is needed. Do not prune in spring.

**Seasonal Value**  Foliage, flowers, fruit, fall color

**Shape**  Variable, often round-topped

**Spread**  30 to 50 feet or more

**Height**  30 to 95 feet

**Soil**  Tolerant, but best if deep, rich, moist

**Use**  Specimen. Most important hardwood on the West Coast. Shade.

**Origin**  From the mountains of southern California to the southern tip of Alaska.

**Comments**  Older trees have bark that is pale gray to reddish-brown, fairly thin. Wood is curly, wavy-grained. Produces burls. Easy to work. Used for interior finish, veneer, tool handles, furniture, posts, etc. Important forage for deer, cattle, horses.

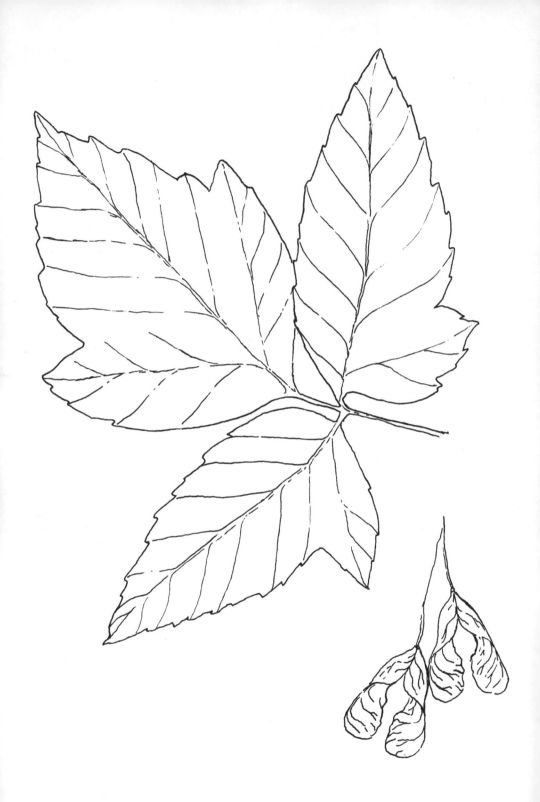

# Acer negundo var. californicum

**Common Name**   California Box Elder

**Family**   Aceraceae

**Leaves**   Deciduous. Opposite. Pinnately compound, with three leaflets.
The terminal one is 3 to 5 lobed. Ovate. Coarsely serrate. Long petioled.
Densely pubescent below and when young. Turning yellow in the fall.
Leaflets 2 to 4 inches long.

**Flowers**   Dioecious. Appearing before the leaves. Greenish. March to April.

**Fruit**   Double samara. Nearly parallel. Finely pubescent to glabrous. Reddish
when young, tan when mature.

**Environment**   Along stream banks and valley bottoms usually below 6000 feet.

**Pests**   Aphids, Box Elder Bug

**Progagation**   Seed, cuttings. Stratify seed for 3 months.

**Rate of Growth**   Rapid

**Pruning**   As needed. Not in the spring.

**Seasonal Value**   Foliage, flowers, fruit, fall color

**Shape**   Round, dense

**Spread**   50 or more feet

**Height**   20 to 40 feet

**Soil**   Tolerant. Deep roots.

**Use**   For quick-growing shade. For hobby work, charcoal.

**Origin**   In the Coast ranges and from the San Bernardino Mountains (Santa
Barbara and Kern counties) to Shasta and Siskiyou counties.

**Comments**   Will stump-sprout. The Box Elder Bug is a serious nuisance.

# *Adenostoma fasciculatum*

**Common Name**  Chamise, Greasewood

**Family**  Rosaceae

**Leaves**  Evergreen. Mostly fascicled. Some Alternate. Olive green. Linear. Glabrous, acute. Often resinous.  About ½ inch in length. Stipules small. Entire.

**Flowers**  White. With pale yellow stamens. Feathery. Sessile. In compact panicles at ends of branches. ½ to 4 inches long. February to July.

**Fruit**  Small achenes.

**Environment**  Coast ranges and Sierra Nevada Mountains to Lower California. In hot, dry areas. Below 5000 feet. Full sun.

**Pests**  Aphids

**Propagation**  Seed, cuttings (burn over the seed bed)

**Rate of Growth**  Moderate

**Pruning**  As desired

**Seasonal Value**  Foliage, flowers

**Shape**  Upright. Has a conspicuous basal burl.

**Spread**  5 feet

**Height**  2 to 10 feet

**Soil**  Dry

**Use**  Specimen

**Origin**  Is the most abundant shrub of the higher California mountains between the lower foothills and the *Pinus ponderosa* belt.  From Mendocino County to Baja California, Sierra Nevada foothills.

**Comments**  *A. sparsifolium* is found in the Chaparral region from Santa Barbara County south to Baja California at from 2000 to 6000 feet.  The leaves are scattered and the flowers are pedicelled.  Both species are very flammable.

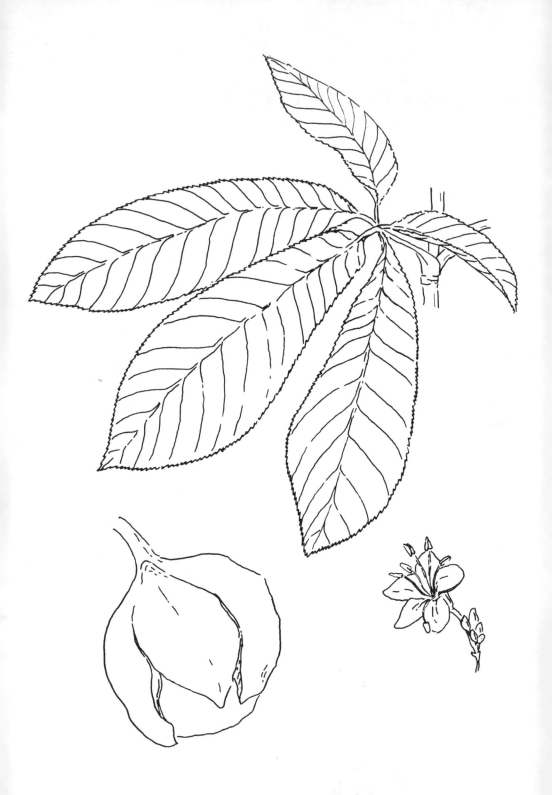

# Aesculus californica

**Common Name**  California Buckeye, Horsechestnut

**Family**  Hippocastanaceae

**Leaves**  Deciduous. With long petioles. Opposite. Palmately compound. With 5 to 7 leaflets usually. These are 3 to 6 inches long, 1½ to 2 inches wide. Nearly glabrous. Leaflets toothed and oblong to lanceolate.

**Flowers**  Pinkish-white. About ½ inch across. In panicles 6 to 10 inches long. May to June. Fragrant. At ends of branches. Toxic to honeybees.

**Fruit**  Pear-shaped capsules. 1½ to 2½ inches long. With 1 or 2 large glossy brown seeds. Poisonous unless treated by leaching with boiling hot water. several times. In the Fall.

**Environment**  Best in cool coastal areas. Full sun or partial shade. Tolerant to wind and seacoast conditions. Grows naturally to 5000 feet.

**Pests**  Caterpillars, mites, scale insects.

**Propagation**  Seed, cuttings

**Rate of Growth**  Moderate

**Pruning**  Only when necessary

**Seasonal Value**  Foliage (short-lived) and trunk and bark. Winter effect.

**Shape**  Broad, variable

**Spread**  30 to 60 feet; Diameter 6 to 15 inches

**Height**  15 to 40 feet

**Soil**  Best in moist, well-drained loam. Tolerant to drought, but will hold foliage longer with moisture. With shallow, spreading roots.

**Use**  Shade, erosion control, specimen. For slopes.

**Origin**  Sierra Foothills and Coast Ranges from Kern and Los Angeles Counties to Siskiyou and Shasta Counties.

**Comments**  Foliage dies early in the season. Good for about two months. Mash from the seed used to stupefy fish.

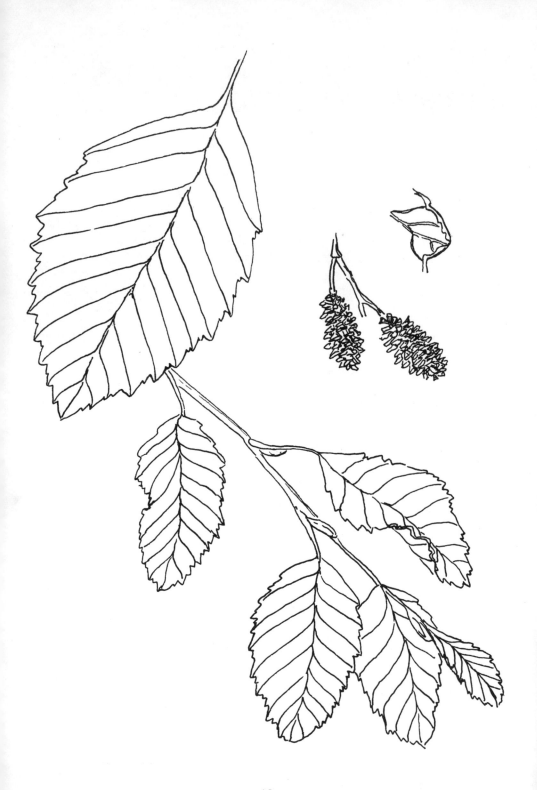

# Alnus oregona

**Common Name**  Red Alder, Oregon Alder, Western Alder

**Family**  Betulaceae

**Leaves**  Deciduous. Ovate to elliptic. Slightly lobed. Coarsely serrate. Dark green above. Revolute. Yellowish-green and sparsely hairy above. Rusty-hairy below. 2½ to 6 inches long, 1½ to 3 inches wide.

**Flowers**  In spring, with or before the leaves. Male are 5 to 6 inches long. Female develop into woody cones. March and April.

**Fruit**  Cones are from ½ to 1 inch long and from one-third to one-half inch across. With 50 to 100 small flattened nut-like seeds.

**Environment**  In humid climate. An annual rainfall of over 25 inches best, unless close to the ocean. From zero to 105 degrees. From sea level to 2500 feet.

**Pests**  Aphids, Caterpillars

**Propagation**  Seed, cuttings. Best germination in full sun.

**Rate of Growth**  Rapid

**Pruning**  To shape when young

**Seasonal Value**  Foliage, flowers, fruit, bark

**Shape**  Upright, branching

**Spread**  20 to 30 feet; Diameter 24 to 30 inches

**Height**  100 to 130 feet

**Soil**  From gravel to sandy or clay. Best in deep, well-drained loam or loamy sand of alluvial origin. In California usually along stream beds.

**Use**  Specimen. Furniture, veneer, cabinet work, shoe soles. Indians used bark for dyes. Wood for smoking salmon.

**Origin**  Pacific Coast region from Santa Barbara north, southeast Alaska to Western British Columbia, and south through Washington, northern Idaho, and western Oregon.

**Comments**  Is the largest species and the most important hardwood of the Pacific Northwest and coastal Alaska. Young trees will stump sprout. Alders help to improve the soil both physically and chemically. The litter decomposes rapidly. The root nodules fix nitrogen. Leaves are high in nitrogen also. Wood has a fine cherry-like grain. Nearly white when cut. Turns darker when exposed to air. Fairly light weight. Easy to work. Bark whitish. Inner bark reddish-brown.

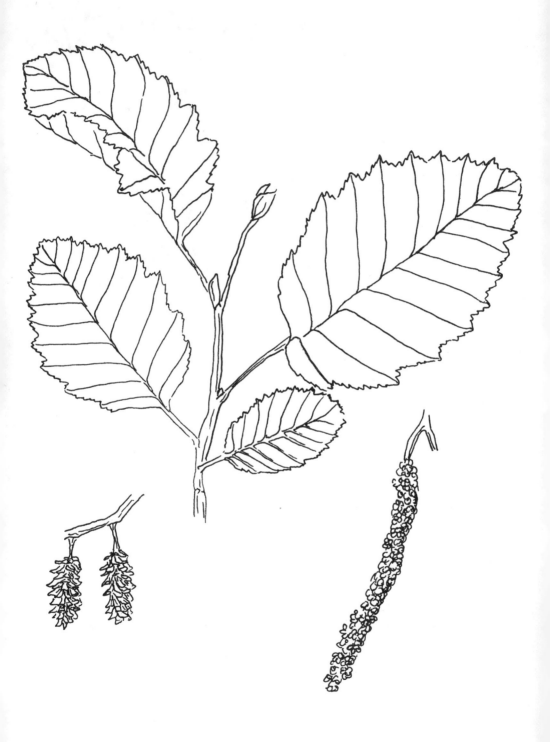

# Alnus rhombifolia

**Common Name**  White Alder

**Family**  Betulaceae

**Leaves**  Deciduous. Alternate. 2 to 3½ inches long, to 2 inches wide. Dark green and glossy above. Finely to coarsly serrate. Pubescent below. Not revolute. Petioles ½ to ¾ inches long.

**Flowers**  Male flowers in catkins, before the leaves. Female flowers develop into woody cones. January to April.

**Fruit**  Cones from three-eighths to five-eighths of an inch long. During the winter.

**Environment**  Grows naturally along stream banks, from sea-level to 5000 feet.

**Pests**  Aphids, caterpillars

**Propagation**  Seed, cuttings

**Rate of Growth**  Rapid

**Pruning**  None usually necessary

**Seasonal Value**  Foliage, cones

**Shape**  Spreading or upright branches, often pendulous at tips

**Spread**  To 40 feet

**Height**  40 to 100 feet

**Soil**  Moist. Has invasive roots. Develop deeper roots by deep watering.

**Use**  Specimen. Quick effect.

**Origin**  Not on immediate coast but most of California north to British Columbia and to Idaho.

**Comments**  Has whitish or grayish-brown bark. With irregular plates on the older trees. Bark used for tea and for a red dye. Leaves used for fleas, burns, eyewash. Alder shoots used for arrows, roots for baskets.

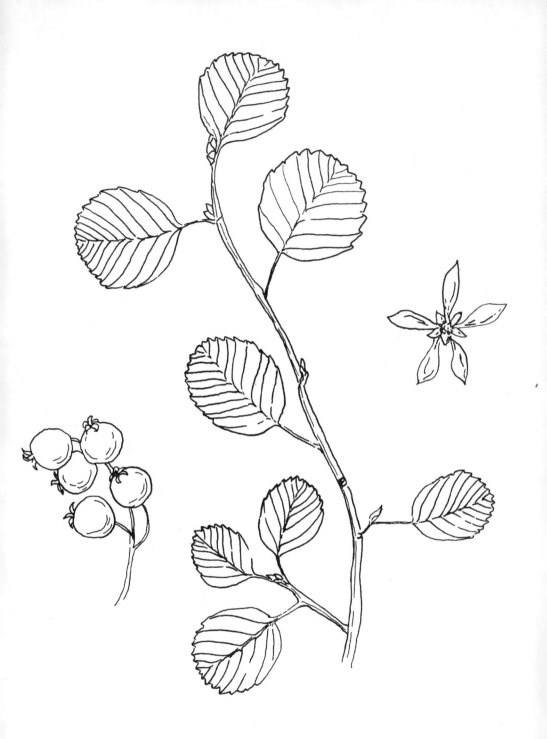

# Amelanchier alnifolia

**Common Name**  Western Service Berry

**Family**  Rosaceae

**Leaves**  Deciduous, alternate. Oval to elliptic to cordate. Entire or serrate above the middle. Variable. New growth bronzy. Green in summer, yellow to reddish in the fall. ¾ to 1¾ inches long, ½ to 1 inch wide. Hairy on both sides.

**Flowers**  White. In racemes. 1 to 2 inches long. May to June.

**Fruit**  Bluish or purplish berry-like pome. To ¼ inch across. Juicy and edible. June to July.

**Environment**  Dry areas of mountain slopes and flats. Tolerant to wide range in elevation, but below 11,000 feet. Full sun.

**Pests**  Aphids

**Propagation**  Seed, cuttings. Stratify seed 3 months.

**Rate of Growth**  Moderate

**Pruning**  As needed

**Seasonal Value**  Foliage, flowers, fruit, fall color

**Shape**  Shrub or small tree

**Spread**  6 to 8 feet or more

**Height**  4 to 15 feet

**Soil**  Dry and rocky best

**Use**  Effective for all seasons. Showy flowers in the spring, fruit in the summer, fall color, branches in winter.

**Origin**  From sea level to sub-alpine regions. Coast ranges and Sierras from Kern and Ventura Counties north to Oregon and west to Nevada.

**Comments**  Bark reddish-brown to grayish. A very variable plant.

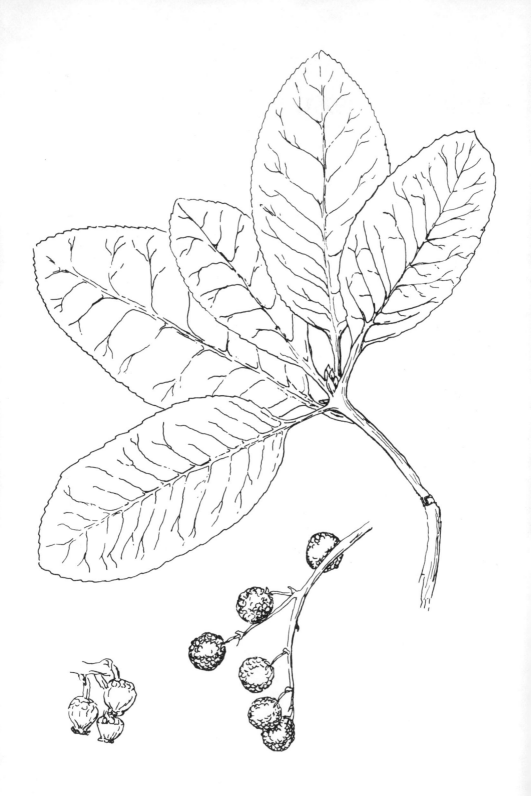

# Arbutus menziesii

**Common Name**  Pacific Madrone

**Family**  Ericaceae

**Leaves**  Evergreen. Thick and leathery. Elliptic to oblong to ovate. Dark green and shiny above. Glaucous below. Entire or serrulate. 3 to 6 inches long, 1¾ to 2¾ inches wide.

**Flowers**  White. Urn-shaped. Waxy. One-third inch long. Slightly fragrant. In terminal panicles which are 3 to 9 inches long and 6 inches across. Source of honey. March to May.

**Fruit**  Edible. Orange to reddish berries, one-third to one-half inch across. Late summer to fall.

**Environment**  From sea level to 6,000 feet. Tolerant to a wide range of climatic conditions. Best in warm, fairly moist locations such as the fog belt. Tolerant to heat, cold, drought. Full sun, partial shade.

**Pests**  Aphids, Madrone Psyllid, caterpillars, wood borers, various leaf diseases, root rot, crown rot, especially Phytophthora spp.

**Propagation**  Seed, cuttings. Stratify seed for 3 months.

**Rate of Growth**  Moderate to slow

**Pruning**  As needed

**Seasonal Value**  Foliage, flowers, fruit, bark

**Shape**  Variable - from low, shrubby, to large, round-headed

**Spread**  15 to 75 feet

**Height**  to 80 feet

**Soil**  Usually grows on glacial till or rocky soils or sandy soils. Tolerant to moist situations and to drought. pH range 4.5 to 7.0.

**Use**  Specimen. Wood for charcoal. Suitable for cabinet work.

**Origin**  Pacific Coast. California, Oregon, Washington, British Columbia.

**Comments**  Very attractive, with the dark green foliage, reddish-brown bark. Not of commercial value for lumber, but used for tools, furniture, novelties. Difficult to work. Is fine-grained, dense, heavy, usually brittle. May warp and/or split. Is a pale reddish-brown color. Commonly seen from San Luis Obispo to Del Norte, Siskiyou Counties and from Mariposa to Shasta County to British Columbia.

# Arctostaphylos densiflora

**Common Name**   Vine Hill Manzanita, Sonoma Manzanita

**Family**   Ericaceae

**Leaves**   Evergreen. Alternate. Bright green. Elliptic to oblong. Entire. Glabrous except along the margins and veins. To 1 inch long and from ¼ to five-eighths inches wide. Stomata both sides. Branches blackish.

**Flowers**   Pink to white. Urn-shaped. About three-sixteenths inches long. In short, dense panicles. March and April.

**Fruit**   Reddish-brown berries. Globular and flattened. About ¼ inch across. Summer.

**Environment**   Full sun, partial shade.

**Pests**   Aphids, Greedy Scale

**Propagation**   Seed, cuttings, layering.   Tip cuttings best.

**Rate of Growth**   Moderate to rapid

**Pruning**   Cut back slightly when young, to shape.

**Seasonal Value**   Foliage, flowers, fruit, bark

**Shape**   Low, spreading, trailing

**Spread**   4 to 6 feet

**Height**   1½ to 6 feet

**Soil**   Tolerant. Best with some summer watering.

**Use**   Group plantings, over walls, on slopes. Ground cover.

**Origin**   From a small area in the Vine Hill region of Sonoma County.

**Comments**   Cultivars: *A. densiflora*   'Harmony', 2 to 3 feet high
'Howard McMinn', 1 to 3 feet high
'Sentinel', 4 to 6 feet high

# Arctostaphylos edmundsii

**Common Name**  Little Sur Manzanita

**Family**  Ericaceae

**Leaves**  Evergreen. Alternate. Roundish, ovate to elliptic. Entire. Light yellow-green. ¾ to 1¼ inches long. No stomata upper side.

**Flowers**  Pink. In clusters. November and December.

**Fruit**  Reddish-brown berries. ¼ inch across. Late spring to early summer.

**Environment**  Full sun or partial shade.

**Pests**  Aphids, Greedy Scale

**Propagation**  Seed, cuttings, layering. Tip cuttings best.

**Rate of Growth**  Moderate

**Pruning**  Cut back slightly when young to form shape.

**Seasonal Value**  Foliage, flowers, fruit, bark

**Shape**  Prostrate

**Spread**  8 feet or more

**Height**  ½ to 2 feet

**Soil**  Tolerant. Needs regular irrigation. Tolerant to salt spray.

**Use**  Ground cover. Border. Over a wall. Below a tree.

**Origin**  Hurricane Point area of Monterey County. At mouth of Little Sur River. River.

**Comments**  No basal burl present. Branches not shreddy. Cultivar 'Little Sur'.

# Arctostaphylos hookeri

**Common Name**  Hooker Manzanita, Monterey Manzanita

**Family**  Ericaceae

**Leaves**  Evergreen. Alternate. Bright green. Elliptic or ovate to obovate. ½ to 1 inch long. Three-eighths to one-half inch wide. Glabrous and with stomata on both sides. Entire. Mucronate. Branches reddish-brown.

**Flowers**  White to pink. Usually a little more than ¼ inch long. In short, nearly head-like racemes. February to April.

**Fruit**  Glossy reddish-brown berries. Roundish. About three-sixteenths of an inch across. Glabrous.

**Environment**  Full sun or partial shade. Tolerant to salt spray. Grows in sand dunes and in wooded areas.

**Pests**  Aphids, Greedy Scale

**Propagation**  Cuttings, seed. Tip cuttings best.

**Rate of Growth**  Moderate

**Pruning**  Little needed.

**Seasonal Value**  Foliage, flowers, berries, bark

**Shape**  Low rounded mounds

**Spread**  6 to 8 feet

**Height**  ½ to 3 feet

**Soil**  Any soil. Tolerates drought.

**Use**  Ground cover. Bank cover. Rock gardens. Foreground. Border.

**Origin**  Monterey Peninsula and Mt. Davidson.

**Comments**  Cultivars: 'Monterey Carpet', 1 foot high
'Wayside', 30 inches high
The parent plant forms conspicuous mounds on the sandy flats and in the open Pine woods in the vicinity of Monterey Bay and also on Mt. Davidson in San Francisco. Has no basal burl.

# Arctostaphylos uva-ursi

**Common Name**  Bearberry, Kinnikinnick, Creeping Manzanita

**Family**  Ericaceae

**Leaves**  Evergreen. Alternate. Entire. About one inch long. Obovate-oblong. Glossy dark green. Thick. Tapering to the petiole. Foliage reddish or bronzy in the winter. Rounded at the apex. See comments.

**Flowers**  White. Tinged with pink. Waxy. Pink at the mouth and green at the stem. Urn-shaped. To one-third of an inch. In dense terminal racemes or panicles. March to June.

**Fruit**  Bright red berries. ¼ inch across. From summer to early winter. July to September.

**Environment**  Does well in full sun or partial shade. Does well on the sandy banks at the seashore. Tolerates to sub-zero. Very hardy. Tolerates hot sun or cool shade. May tip-burn if too dry.

**Pests**  Greedy Scale, Flat-headed Apple Tree Borer, Aphids

**Propagation**  Layering. Seed. Dip seed in boiling water for a few minutes. (tip, heel cuttings)

**Rate of Growth**  Slow to moderate

**Pruning**  Thin out dead or dying wood.

**Seasonal Value**  Foliage, flowers, berries, bark.

**Shape**  Prostrate. Spreading. Self-layers.

**Spread**  To 15 feet

**Height**  6 to 12 inches

**Soil**  Sandy is best. Is drought-tolerant. Needs some summer water. Does well with leaf mold, sand, or gravel.

**Use**  Ground cover. For banks, hillsides. Trailing over rocks, walls. Edges of paths. Fence corners. Containers. Under Pines.

**Origin**  Europe, Asia, North America. In California from San Mateo County north to Alaska.

**Comments**  Reddish-brown branches are a contrast to the bright green foliage. Foliage becomes bronzy in the winter. There are about 50 species native to North and Central America, especially on the Pacific Coast. Stems are dark brown, with the older ones being shreddy. Leaves have been used for medicinal purposes. Fruit is used for jellies and for Cider drinks. Place plants about 3 feet apart from one-gallon cans. Mulch with sawdust to subdue weeds and to retain moisture. Berries may be larger if tips of branches grow up and over some obstacle. Two cultivars: 'Point Reyes' and 'Radiant'. No stomata on upper side of leaves.

# Artemisia pycnocephala

**Common Name**  Coast Sagebrush

**Family**  Compositae

**Leaves**  Herbaceous or woody. Dissected into spatulate or linear lobes. Densely silky hairy. Grayish. Pungent. 1 to 2 inches in length. Entire.

**Flowers**  Whitish. In erect spikes. 2 to 4 inches across. Rising about 12 inches above the rest of the plant. Individual flowers small. Tip of inflorescence pendulous. July to August.

**Fruit**  Hairy achene. August to October.

**Environment**  Full sun. If in shade then is less erect, less gray in color. Common on exposed slopes, dry hills from near sea level to 2500 feet. Not for hot interior valleys.

**Pests**  Aphids

**Propagation**  Seed, cuttings.

**Rate of Growth**  Rapid

**Pruning**  Remove flower stems as they appear. Replace entire plant when it becomes unattractive.

**Seasonal Value**  Foliage, fragrance

**Shape**  Erect, spreading

**Spread**  to 2 feet

**Height**  1½ to 2¼ feet

**Soil**  Tolerant to soil, drought. Should have good drainage.

**Use**  For borders. Where a gray plant is desired. Sunny locations. Effective with red, orange, blue, pink, purple colors.

**Origin**  In the sand hills along the coast. From Monterey to Humboldt Counties and into Oregon.

**Comments**  More compact if flowers removed. Not long-lived. Commonly associated with Eriogonum fasciculatum and Salvia mellifera. Leaves are alternate.

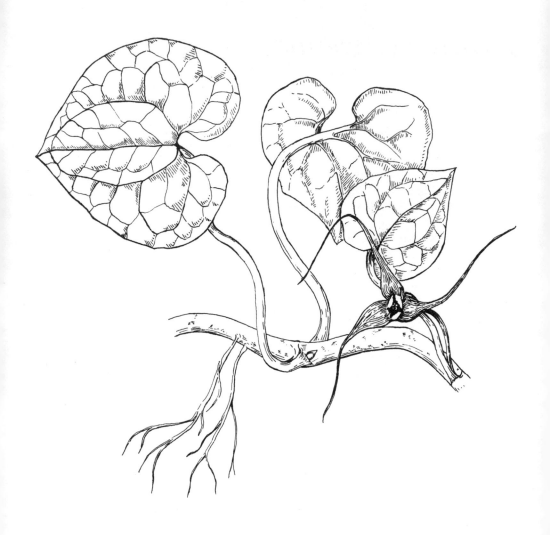

# *Asarum caudatum*

**Common Name**  Wild Ginger

**Family**  Aristolochiaceae

**Leaves**  Evergreen. Herbaceous. Alternate or basal. Cordate to reniform. Entire. Glabrous. Ciliate. Pubescent on upper side and on stems. 2 to 7 inches across. Ginger-like odor.

**Flowers**  Brownish-purple. Sepals only. Long-lasting. Axillary or terminal. Hidden by leaves. 1 to 2½ inches long. May to July.

**Fruit**  A fleshy, globular capsule. Seeds large, compressed.

**Environment**  Best in shade. Tolerant to much shade. Tolerant to below zero. Grows below 5000 feet.

**Pests**  Fungus Leaf Spot, Slugs, Snails

**Propagation**  Division, seed

**Rate of Growth**  Rapid, once established

**Pruning**  Usually not needed. Keep under control.

**Seasonal Value**  Foliage, flowers

**Shape**  Spreading, low

**Spread**  Wide

**Height**  7 to 10 inches

**Soil**  Best with sufficient organic matter, moisture. Spreads by rhizomes.

**Use**  Ground cover. Erosion control.

**Origin**  In the wooded areas of the Coast Ranges, mostly in the Redwood Belt. From the Santa Cruz mountains to Del Norte Country, north to British Columbia.

**Comments**  A very effective ground cover in shaded areas. The roots can be used as a substitute for exotic Ginger. Stems and the roots are aromatic.

# Atriplex lentiformis var. breweri

**Common Name**  Brewer Saltbush

**Family**  Chenopodiaceae

**Leaves**  Evergreen to semi-evergreen. Grayish-green. Roundish to oblong to ovate-deltoid. Entire. 1 to 2 inches long. Fire-resistant. Alternate.

**Flowers**  Greenish. Small. In large branched clusters, monoecious or dioecious. August to October.

**Fruit**  In clusters. May turn brilliant rose to purple.

**Environment**  Full sun. Tolerant to salt spray, alkaline, saline areas.

**Pests**  Aphids

**Propagation**  Cuttings, layering, seed.

**Rate of Growth**  Rapid

**Pruning**  Tolerant to severe pruning. Prune as needed.

**Seasonal Value**  Foliage, fruit

**Shape**  Upright, dense

**Spread**  6 to 10 feet

**Height**  6 to 10 feet

**Soil**  Tolerant. Even alkaline, pure sand, considerable moisture.

**Use**  For mass effect on wind-swept beach. For a wind screen, erosion control. control. Firebreak.

**Origin**  On the coast from San Francisco Bay to Orange County and Hollister, Salinas Valley and West Riverside County.

**Comments**  There are 29 species of Atriplex in California.

# Baccharis pilularis

**Common Name**  Dwarf Coyote Bush

**Family**  Compositae

**Leaves**  Evergreen or semi-evergreen. Alternate. Sessile. Coarsely or sinuately few-toothed. Sometimes entire. Obovate or cuneate. ½ to 1 inch long. Bright green when young. Glabrous.

**Flowers**  Usually clustered in the leaf axils, or terminal. Dioecious. Male flowers yellowish. Female flowers white and create litter. July to September.

**Fruit**  Compressed achenes. Ribbed with pappus.

**Environment**  On low foothills, mountain slopes, coast sand dunes. From sea level to 1500 feet. Full sun or partial shade. Tolerant to growing in sand. To zero degrees.

**Pests**  Aphids, Black Scale, Greedy Scale, Asterolecanium Scale.

**Propagation**  Seed, cuttings, layering. Cuttings best.

**Rate of Growth**  Rapid

**Pruning**  Thin as needed

**Seasonal Value**  Flowers, foliage

**Shape**  Prostrate

**Spread**  2 to 10 feet

**Height**  6 to 12 inches

**Soil**  Deep-rooted. Tolerant, but best in light or sandy soils. Tolerant to drought and to moisture. Irrigate monthly during summer.

**Use**  Erosion control. Ground cover.

**Origin**  From Monterey County to Sonoma County.

**Comments**  Plant 3 feet apart. Responds to nitrogen. Branches angular. Cultivars 'Pigeon Point' and 'Twin Peaks'.

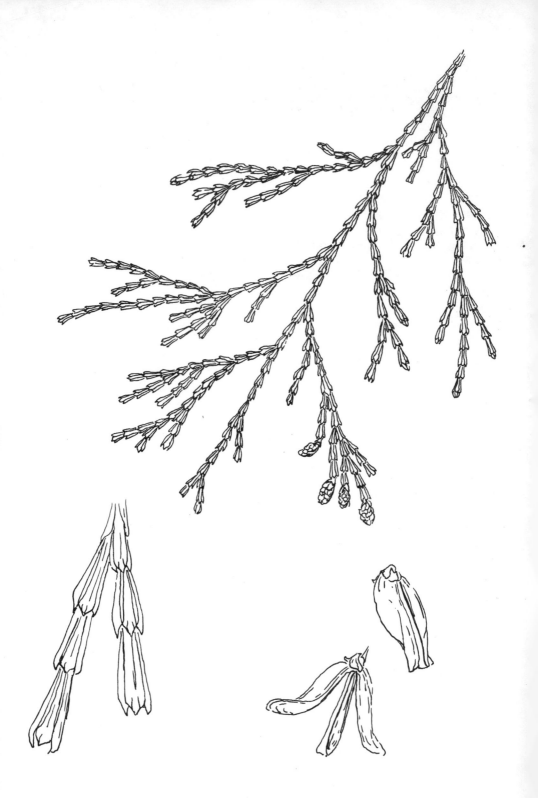

# Calocedrus decurrens

**Common Name**  Incense Cedar

**Family**  Cupressaceae

**Leaves**  Evergreen. Branchlets alternate. In flat, drooping sprays. Scale-like. Opposite. Aromatic. Green to yellowish. One twelfth to ¼ of an inch long. Leaf bases decurrent.

**Flowers**  In solitary and in terminal catkins.

**Fruit**  Cones. Small, oblong to ovoid. Pendulous. Urn-shaped, reddish-brown, ¾ to 1 inch long. Maturing the first year.

**Environment**  Full sun, partial shade. Tolerant to extremes of heat, cold. From 2500 to 7000 feet. On mountain slopes. Naturally where summers are dry and where annual rainfall is from 20 to 80 inches.

**Pests**  Aphids, Leaf Rust, Mistletoe

**Propagation**  Seed, in late fall, early spring. Cuttings in fall. Stratify seed 2 to 3 months.

**Rate of Growth**  Slow to get established, then moderate to rapid

**Pruning**  Only if needed.

**Seasonal Value**  Foliage, fruit

**Shape**  Columnar, with pendulous branches

**Spread**  to 50 feet; diameter from 3 to 7 feet

**Height**  50 to 150 feet

**Soil**  Tolerant. Has a deep root system. Best stands are on deep, well-drained, acid soils.

**Use**  Specimen, windbreak, hedge

**Origin**  From Lower California to the southern slope of Mt. Hood in Oregon.

**Comments**  Wood is soft, compact, light, durable, uniform texture, easy to work. Often used for Cedar Chests. Oil is extracted from the wood and used in the manufacture of perfume. Wood also used for shingles, railroad ties, pencils, lumber, furniture, etc. Bark is a cinnamon-brown color, peels in long strips. Seldom in pure stands except in small areas. Profuse seeding, though not every year. (August and September.) Living to 500 years.

# Calycanthus occidentalis

**Common Name**  Spicebush, Sweet Shrub

**Family**  Calycanthaceae

**Leaves**  Deciduous. Opposite. Entire. Glabrous, or sometimes slightly pubescent. Ovate to oblong to lanceolate. Acute. Rounded at the base. Aromatic. 2 to 6 inches long, 1½ to 2½ inches wide.

**Flowers**  Reddish-brown. Terminal, solitary. Each bloom lasting only one or two days, but others quickly replace them. To 3 inches across. May to November.

**Fruit**  Achene. Containing numerous seeds. Urn-shaped. 1 to 1¼ inches long.

**Environment**  Full sun or partial shade. Usually along stream banks and on moist slopes. 800 to 3800 feet. Partial shade best.

**Pests**  Snails

**Propagation**  Seed, cuttings, division, suckers.

**Rate of Growth**  Rapid

**Pruning**  Only if needed

**Seasonal Value**  Foliage, flowers

**Shape**  Erect, compact

**Spread**  4 to 12 feet

**Height**  4 to 12 feet

**Soil**  Moist. Grows larger if it has sufficient moisture.

**Use**  Specimen, groupings. Background.

**Origin**  In the north coastal ranges and in the Sierra Nevada foothills.

**Comments**  There are 4 species native to north America. Introduced into cultivation in 1831. Bark is aromatic.

# Carpenteria californica

**Common Name**  Bush Anemone

**Family**  Saxifragaceae

**Leaves**  Evergreen. Opposite. Oblong to lanceolate. Tapering at both ends. Whitish below. Margins revolute. Entire or finely toothed. Glabrous above. 2 to 4½ inches long. To 2¼ inches wide.

**Flowers**  White. With yellow stamens. In terminal clusters (cymes). Individual flowers 1½ to 3 inches across. May to August.

**Fruit**  A conical, leathery capsule. With many seeds. Three-eighths to one-half of an inch across.

**Environment**  Full sun or partial shade. Probably best in some shade. From 2000 to 3000 feet.

**Pests**  Aphids, mites. New foliage often curled from aphid or from mite injury.

**Propagation**  Seed, cuttings, suckers. Plant the tiny seed in a thin layer of sphagnum moss and place this on the soil mixture.

**Rate of Growth**  Slow

**Pruning**  If needed.

**Seasonal Value**  Foliage, flowers, fragrance

**Shape**  Upright, compact

**Spread**  4 to 6 feet

**Height**  6 to 8 to 15 feet

**Soil**  Well-drained soil. Tolerant to some water.

**Use**  Specimen, mass effect. Under large trees. Effective with Ceanothus, Mahonia, Manzanita, Redbud, Rhododendrons, etc.

**Origin**  In the foothills of the Sierra Nevadas.

**Comments**  The bark is tan-colored. Best to select red-stemmed forms. They produce flower clusters that are more open, and the red stems are more colorful. Introduced into cultivation about 1875.

# Ceanothus gloriosus

**Common Name**  Point Reyes Creeper

**Family**  Rhamnaceae

**Leaves**  Evergreen. Opposite, toothed. Blades broadly elliptic, round or broadly oblong. ½ to 1½ inches long, three-eighths to one inch wide. Cuneate or obtuse base. Thick, leathery. Dark green and glabrous above. Margins dentate or spinosely toothed, or entire. 1-veined from base.

**Flowers**  Deep blue to purple, in clusters composed of many sessile umbels on short axillary stems. March to May.

**Fruit**  Small globose capsules in clusters. Each about one-eighth inch across. Viscid. 3-horned at the top.

**Environment**  Full sun or partial shade. Tolerant to wind, salt spray.

**Pests**  Aphids, Flat-headed Borer, Greedy Scale, Ivy Scale

**Propagation**  Seed, cuttings, layering. Treat seed with hot water.

**Rate of Growth**  Moderate to rapid

**Pruning**  Thin as needed

**Seasonal Value**  Foliage, flowers

**Shape**  Low, spreading mat

**Spread**  5 feet or more

**Height**  4 to 20 inches or more

**Soil**  Sandy or well-drained best. Tolerant to some moisture.

**Use**  Ground cover, bank cover, over low walls. In rock gardens, along paths.

**Origin**  From Marin to Mendocino Counties. Immediate coastal area.

**Comments**  Almost 60 species. All native to North America, with 40 being native to the Pacific area. Flowers when crushed and rubbed in water give a soapy lather. The foliage of *C. americanus* (an eastern species) was made into a beverage by the Indians. Was called New Jersey tea. Plant 3 feet apart on slopes. Cultivar 'Anchor Bay'.

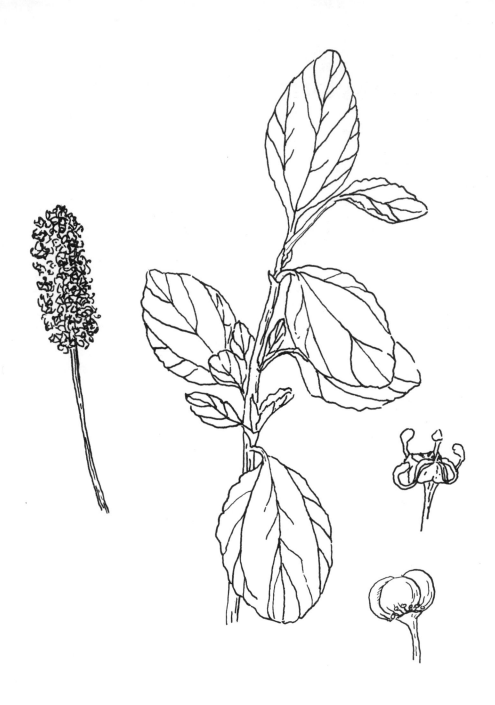

# Ceanothus griseus var. horizontalis

**Common Name**  Carmel Creeper

**Family**  Rhamnaceae

**Leaves**  Evergreen. Alternate. Toothed. 3 distinct veins from the base. Broadly ovate. Usually grayish-silky below. Branchlets angled. Obtuse. Dark green above. Revolute. 1 to 2 inches long, about 1 inch wide.

**Flowers**  Violet blue. In dense panicles. ¾ to 2 inches long. February to May.

**Fruit**  Nearly round. Glandular and viscid when immature. Black and shiny when mature. A dry capsule.

**Environment**  Full sun or partial shade. To 10 degrees. May die out in very hot locations, especially if kept too dry.

**Pests**  Aphids, Greedy Scale, Asterolecanium Scale, Mealybug

**Propagation**  Cuttings. Treat seed with hot water.

**Rate of Growth**  Moderate to rapid

**Pruning**  As needed. Thin occasionally. Tolerant to severe pruning. Is a rampant grower.

**Seasonal Value**  Foliage, flowers

**Shape**  Low, creeping

**Spread**  5 to 15 feet

**Height**  3 to 5 feet or more

**Soil**  Tolerant to poor, dry soil, but needs good drainage.

**Use**  Ground cover, bank cover, containers, rock gardens

**Origin**  Coastal Monterey County

**Comments**  Keep the crown dry. Water no more than once a month. Do not allow the soil to build up around the crown of any ceanothus.
Cultivars include 'Louis Edmunds', 4 to 6 feet high
'Yankee Point', 2 to 3 feet high

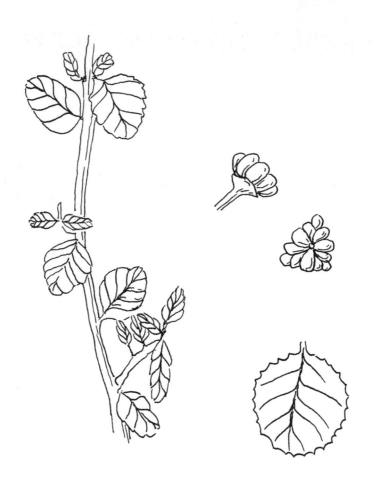

# Ceanothus impressus

**Common Name**  Santa Barbara Ceanothus

**Family**  Rhamnaceae

**Leaves**  Evergreen. Dark green. Wrinkled. Alternate. ¼ to ½ inch long. Narrow. Elliptic to orbicular. Entire or toothed. One-veined from the base. Pubescent. Young growth densely pubescent. Upper side deeply grooved along the veins. Revolute.

**Flowers**  Deep blue. In Panicles which are from ½ to 1 inch long. February to April.

**Fruit**  A dry capsule. About ¼ inch across.

**Environment**  Full sun or partial shade. Chaparral areas.

**Pests**  Aphids, Greedy Scale, Asterolecanium Scale

**Propagation**  Seed, cuttings (treat seed with hot water)

**Rate of Growth**  Rapid

**Pruning**  As needed. To prevent from getting too leggy.

**Seasonal Value**  Foliage, flowers

**Shape**  Upright, densely branched

**Spread**  8 to 10 feet

**Height**  3 to 5 feet

**Soil**  Best in sandy or rocky soil, with good drainage.

**Use**  Specimen. Ground cover. On dry slopes.

**Origin**  A limited area in Santa Barbara and San Luis Obispo Counties.

**Comments**  Cultivar: 'Julia Phelps'

# *Ceanothus purpureus*

**Common Name**  Hollyleaf Ceanothus
**Family**  Rhamnaceae
**Leaves**  Evergreen. Opposite. Dark green above. Grayish below. Elliptic to orbicular. With undulate and spiny-toothed margins. ½ to ¾ inches long. One-veined from base.
**Flowers**  Bluish-purple. In several-flowered umbels. February to April.
**Fruit**  Capsules with black seeds
**Environment**  Dry rocky hills. Below 1800 feet.
**Pests**  Aphids, Greedy Scale, Asterolecanium Scale
**Propagation**  Seed, cuttings. Hot water on seed.
**Rate of Growth**  Moderate
**Pruning**  As needed
**Seasonal Value**  Foliage, flowers
**Shape**  Erect, spreading
**Spread**  5 to 6 feet or more
**Height**  2 to 4 feet
**Soil**  Tolerant. Should be well-drained
**Use**  Ground cover
**Origin**  Napa County
**Comments**  Branches reddish-brown

# Cercis occidentalis

**Common Name**  Western Redbud

**Family**  Leguminosae

**Leaves**  Deciduous. Alternate. Nearly round. Cordate at the base. Entire. Green when young, dark bluish-green later. Yellow to red in the fall. New growth is copper-colored. Notched or rounded at the apex. 2 to 3½ inches across.

**Flowers**  Magenta-colored. On short stalks of from 6 to 12 flowers. Before the leaves. Last about three weeks. Best if temperature goes below 28 degrees in the winter season. March to April.

**Fruit**  Oblong pods. Flattened. Dull red color. Seeds maturing in the fall. 1½ to 3 inches long, with 3 to 4 seeds. May to August.

**Environment**  Full sun or partial shade. Effective on dry slopes. Grows most places except in desert areas.

**Pests**  Scales (Black, Greedy, etc.), Leafhoppers, Caterpillars, White Fly, Oak Root Fungus, Leaf Spot, Root Rot, Crown Gall

**Propagation**  Seed, cuttings. Use boiling water on seeds, soak for 24 hours or stratify for 2 months.

**Rate of Growth**  Rapid

**Pruning**  To shape, if necessary

**Seasonal Value**  Foliage, flowers, fruit, fall color

**Shape**  Compact, multi-branched

**Spread**  to 16 feet

**Height**  8 to 20 feet

**Soil**  Best if slightly acid. Good drainage essential.

**Use**  Specimen, groupings, background. Effective with other natives such as *Ceanothus griseus*.

**Origin**  Mostly in the south central part of California, between 1000 and 4500 feet. Also in the Sierra Foothills and the Coast Ranges.

**Comments**  Widespread in California. Cultivated since 1886. Branches are often reddish-purple. Interesting plant all year. Fruit persists a long time. Indians used the astringent bark for Diarrhea and Dysentery, also the bark of young shoots for making baskets. Young buds used for salads or were pickled. Wood takes a fine polish.

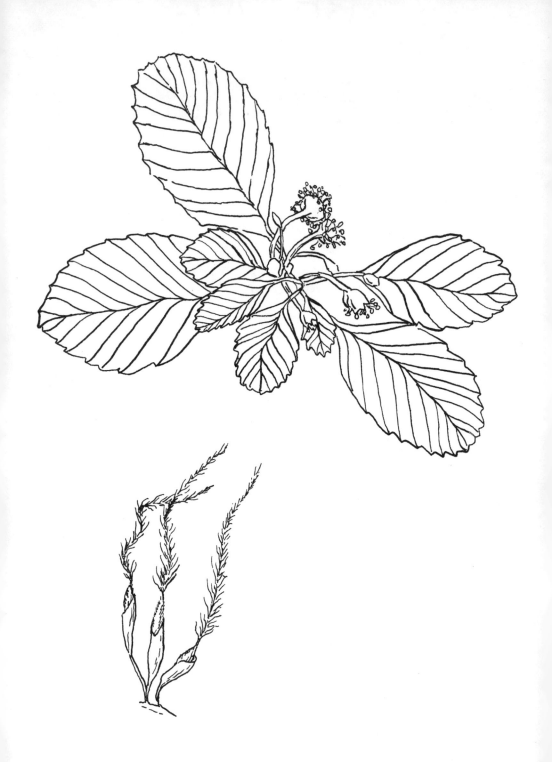

# *Cercocarpus betuloides var. traskiae*

**Common Name**  Catalina Mountain Mahogany, Catalina Hard-tack

**Family**  Rosaceae

**Leaves**  Evergreen or semi-evergreen. Alternate. Elliptic to ovate. Thick and leathery. Coarsely toothed except at the base. Dark green above, white hairy below. 1½ to 2¼ inches long.

**Flowers**  Small, inconspicuous. Solitary or several in the leaf axils. Fragrant and attractive to bees. March to May. White.

**Fruit**  Long, hairy, twisted. June to August.

**Environment**  Full sun or partial shade. On dry slopes and in washes.

**Pests**  Aphids

**Propagation**  Seed, cuttings. Self-sows.

**Rate of Growth**  Moderate

**Pruning**  Encourage new growth by removing some larger branches each year.

**Seasonal Value**  Foliage, fruit

**Shape**  A large erect shrub or small tree

**Spread**  15 feet or more

**Height**  to 25 feet

**Soil**  Tolerant except where very alkaline. Dry.

**Use**  On dry sunny slopes. Informal hedge. Background.

**Origin**  Only from Santa Catalina and Santa Cruz Islands.

**Comments**  The young shoots are reddish-brown and very hairy. The wood is hard and tough. Makes a hot fire. Used by the Indians for fish spears, arrow shafts and for pointed sticks for digging. The inner bark makes a purple dye. The bark was used in a tea for curing colds. The powdered young plants, stirred in water were used as a laxative. The Spanish-Americans, to discourage bedbugs, would hang a branch near their beds. There are 20 species native to the West.

# Cercocarpus ledifolius

**Common Name**  Curl-Leaf Mountain Mahogany, Desert Mountain Mahogany

**Family**  Rosaceae

**Leaves**  Evergreen. Alternate. Leathery. Resinous. Dark green above. Entire. White hairy below. Narrower than *C. betuloides*. ½ to 1 inch long. To ½ inch in width. Revolute. Lanceolate to Oblanceolate. Thick, leathery.

**Flowers**  Small. Solitary or several in the leaf axils. March to May. White.

**Fruit**  Long, hairy, twisted. Late summer, early fall.

**Environment**  Full sun or partial shade. Grows on mountain slopes and on flat areas at elevations of from 4000 to 9000 feet.

**Pests**  Aphids

**Propagation**  Seed, cuttings. Stratify seed 1 to 3 months.

**Rate of Growth**  Rapid

**Pruning**  As needed

**Seasonal Value**  Foliage, fruit

**Shape**  Small tree with an open top

**Spread**  15 feet or more; Diameter to 2 feet

**Height**  To 30 feet

**Soil**  Tolerant to poor, dry soil

**Use**  Specimen in colder areas

**Origin**  From southern California in the desert regions and also in the Western States east of the Sierra-Nevada-Cascade Ranges.

**Comments**  Wood is hard, dense, brittle, fine and straight-grained. When cut, the heartwood is a mahogany-red, which turns to pale, reddish-brown. Sapwood is pale yellow to creamy white. Wood checks and warps badly. Difficult to work with hand tools. No commercial value except for local use as fence posts, firewood, novelties. Branches are strong and intricately twisted. Bark is smooth and gray on young branches. On mature branches, it becomes dark and furrowed.

# Chamaecyparis lawsoniana

**Common Name**  Lawson Cypress, Port Orford Cedar

**Family**  Cupressaceae

**Leaves**  Evergreen. Bright green above, glaucous below. Glandular above. Soft to the touch. In flat sprays. Leaves one-sixteenth inch long. Scale-like. Opposite in pairs.

**Flowers**  Male flowers are bright red catkins.

**Fruit**  Small, shiny brown cones. ¼ inch across. With 8 to 10 scales, each with 2 to 4 seeds.

**Environment**  Full sun or partial shade. Best in cool, coastal areas. Not tolerant to hot, dry winds or very cold climates. Grows naturally where winters are wet and summers dry, with frequent summer fog. To 4800 feet.

**Pests**  Aphids, Bark Beetle

**Propagation**  Seed, cuttings

**Rate of Growth**  Moderate to rapid

**Pruning**  Usually not necessary

**Seasonal Value**  Foliage, fruit

**Shape**  Pyramidal, formal

**Spread**  30 to 50 feet; diameter to 6 feet

**Height**  75 to 100 or even to 200 feet

**Soil**  Does well in moist soils. Best if moderately moist, well-drained, sandy loam. Tolerant to some drought.

**Use**  Specimen, container, accent. Valued timber tree. Wood is strong, hard, durable, resinous, light, aromatic.. Easy to work. Used for moth-proof chests, flooring, doors, furniture, etc.

**Origin**  Northwestern California to southwestern Oregon

**Comments**  There are many cultivars derived from this tree. One is *C. lawsoniana* 'Stewartii'. Grows to 30 feet. New growth is yellow and older growth is green.

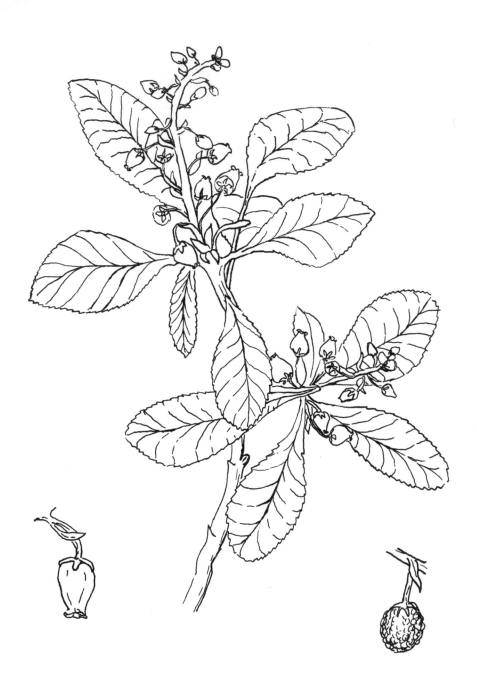

# Comarostaphylis diversifolia

**Common Name**  Summer Holly

**Family**  Ericaceae

**Leaves**  Evergreen. Alternate. Leathery. Elliptic to ovate. 1 to 3 inches in length. Dark green. Glossy above. Pubescent below. Toothed. Margins revolute.

**Flowers**  Loose clusters of white waxy bell-like flowers. Terminal and solitary or in racemes or panicles. May to June.

**Fruit**  Red warty berries. Similar to Madrone. ¼ inch. In clusters. August to September. Birds enjoy.

**Environment**  Full sun or part shade. Best in partial shade with some moisture. Grows on dry slopes near the coast.

**Pests**  Greedy Scale, Mealybug

**Propagation**  Seed, cuttings. Treat seed with hot water or stratify 3 months.

**Rate of Growth**  Moderate

**Pruning**  Only if necessary

**Seasonal Value**  Foliage, flowers, fruit.

**Shape**  Large shrub or small tree; compact.

**Spread**  4 to 8 feet

**Height**  6 to 18 feet

**Soil**  Drought-tolerant, but best with some water in summer.

**Use**  In small groves. Background. Screen. Hedge. Effective with Pines, Ceanothus, Pacific Wax Myrtle, Ironwood, etc.

**Origin**  Coastal Southern California (San Diego County) and Baja California.

**Comments**  Gray shreddy bark.

# Cornus nuttallii

**Common Name**  Pacific Dogwood

**Family**  Cornaceae

**Leaves**  Deciduous. Opposite. Thin. Elliptic to obovate to nearly orbicular. Bright green and slightly hairy above. White hairy below. Entire or slightly toothed. 3 to 5 inches long and from 1½ to 3 inches wide. Petioles ¼ to ½ inch long.

**Flowers**  Green. Forming a head. Surrounded by white bracts which are petal-like and are from 2 to 3 inches long. April to July.

**Fruit**  Red drupes. In clusters. ½ inch long (each). Ellipsoidal.

**Environment**  In temperate areas. Best in partial shade. In lower slopes and bottom areas where there is some moisture. From 200 to 6000 feet.

**Pests**  Aphids

**Propagation**  Seed, cuttings. Stratify for 3 months.

**Rate of Growth**  Slow

**Pruning**  Usually not necessary

**Seasonal Value**  Foliage, flowers, bark, fall color

**Shape**  Upright, branching. Large shrub or a tree

**Spread**  to 20 feet; diameter to 2 feet

**Height**  30 to 50 feet

**Soil**  Moist and well-drained

**Use**  Specimen. Wood is used for cabinet work, tool handles.

**Origin**  Grows from southern California to British Columbia to Idaho.

**Comments**  The name *Dogwood* was derived from the fact that the bark has been used for mange in dogs. The bark contains a substitute for quinine - used during the Civil War. The wood is also used for the hubs of small wheels, wood engraving blocks, golf club handles, etc. Brilliant red foliage in the winter season. Bark effective for winter design.

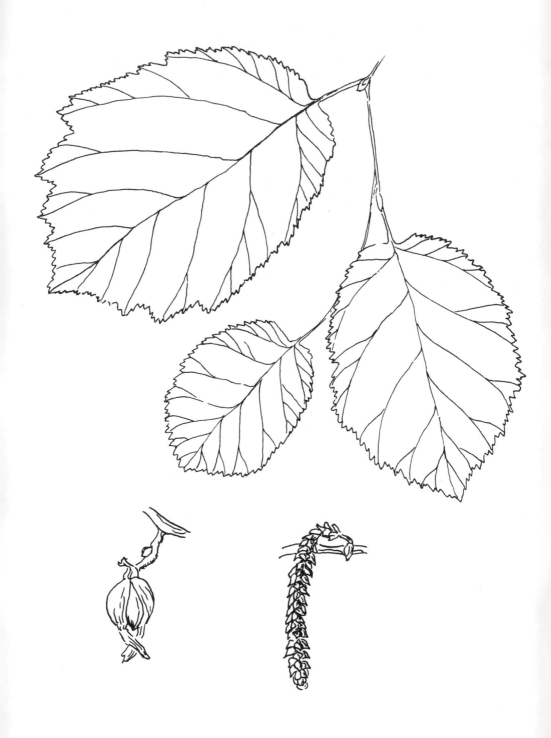

# Corylus cornuta var. californica

**Common Name**  Hazlenut, Filbert

**Family**  Betulaceae

**Leaves**  Deciduous. Alternate. Orbicular to obovate. 2 to 4 inches long. About as wide. Oblique. Cordate at base. Doubly serrate. Sometimes with three lobes. Pubescent.

**Flowers**  Monoecious. In catkins. Male pendulous with 1 to 3 flowers. Female erect or pendulous. Shorter. January to April.

**Fruit**  Edible. A small one-seeded nutlet. Often cone-like. In clusters.

**Environment**  Native to moist slopes below 7000 feet. Part shade.

**Pests**  Aphids, leafhoppers

**Propagation**  Seed, cuttings. Stratify seed 2 to 3 months.

**Rate of Growth**  Moderate to rapid

**Pruning**  As needed

**Seasonal Value**  Foliage, flowers, fruit

**Shape**  Erect, branching, roundish

**Spread**  5 to 12 feet

**Height**  5 to 12 feet

**Soil**  Tolerant. Best if moist and with sufficient organic matter.

**Use**  Specimen

**Origin**  North Coastal Ranges from Santa Cruz County north to Del Norte County, from Tulare County north to British Columbia.

**Comments**  Bark is smooth

# Cupressus macrocarpa

**Common Name**  Monterey Cypress

**Family**  Cupressaceae

**Leaves**  Evergreen. Opposite. Scale-like. Obtuse, not glandular. Aromatic. Branchlets not distinctly flat. Leaves do not have resin pits.

**Flowers**  Inconspicuous. Monoecious. Solitary on short branchlets. Male catkins yellow. February to April.

**Fruit**  Cones. Subglobose. 1 to 2 inches in diameter. Seeds reddish-brown or light chestnut brown. Mature the second year. Larger than those on Chamaecyparis. Scales usually with 4 or more seeds.

**Environment**  Coastal area. Sun, seacoast, wind-tolerant.

**Pests**  Many, including Cypress Bark Beetle and Cypress Bark Canker, Spittlebug.

**Propagation**  Seed, cuttings

**Rate of Growth**  Rapid, even on poor soils.

**Pruning**  Keep dead wood removed. Thin when necessary.

**Seasonal Value**  Foliage, cones.

**Shape**  Compact, wide-spreading

**Spread**  to 75 feet

**Height**  20 to 75 feet

**Soil**  Any. With good drainage. Best in dry, deep, sandy loam. Has voracious root system.

**Use**  Hedge, windbreak, specimen. Erosion Control.

**Origin**  From Cypress Point Grove to Pescadero Point, another at Point Lobos (smaller grove).

**Comments**  Arizona Cypress is a cleaner tree. In San Mateo County, trees may not be moved into the area west of Skyline and north of Sneath Lane. This line is to protect the Cypress of Golden Gate Park. The wood is hard, strong, heavy and durable. Sometimes used by the California State Division of Highways for windy areas.

# Dendromecon harfordii

**Common Name**  Island Tree Poppy

**Family**  Papaveraceae

**Leaves**  Evergreen. Alternate. Broadly elliptic to oblong to ovate. Entire. Leathery. Grayish or yellowish-green. May be finely toothed. Glabrous. 1 to 3 inches long. To 1½ inches wide.

**Flowers**  Bright yellow. Terminal. Numerous stamens. Fragrant. Most of the year. 2 to 3 inches across. Mostly April to August.

**Fruit**  A long narrow curved capsule. 2 to 4 inches long.

**Environment**  Full sun

**Pests**  Aphids

**Propagation**  Seed or cuttings. Plant seed in light soil mix. Cover with straw or pine needles and burn. Cuttings best when plant is in bloom.

**Rate of Growth**  Moderate

**Pruning**  After bloom. Tolerant to severe pruning but not necessary.

**Seasonal Value**  Foliage, flowers

**Shape**  Variable. Upright. Rounded.

**Spread**  2 to 20 feet

**Height**  2 to 20 feet

**Soil**  Well-drained. Dry. Very little water during the summer.

**Use**  Specimen

**Origin**  Santa Cruz and Santa Rosa Islands off the coast of southern California

**Comments**  Needs excellent drainage. Introduced into cultivation about 1854. Has shreddy bark on stems and larger branches. *D. rigida* is from the mainland.

# Equisetum hyemale

**Common Name**  Horsetail, Common Scouring-Rush

**Family**  Equisetaceae

**Leaves**  Evergreen. Cylindrical. Usually ashy with black bands, one band at base, one at top. Teeth are brown, with whitish margins. Jointed and ridged (8 to 34 ridges). Rush-like.

**Flowers**  No true flowers. Produces spores.

**Fruit**  Cones which are from ½ to 1¼ inches long

**Environment**  Shaded areas. Moist soils from sea level to 8500 feet

**Pests**  Apparently clean

**Propagation**  Spores, rhizomes

**Rate of Growth**  Rapid

**Pruning**  Keep under control

**Seasonal Value**  Foliage, stems

**Shape**  Erect, rigid

**Spread**  Wide

**Height**  2 to 4 feet

**Soil**  Moist. Very invasive. Rhizomes

**Use**  For moist areas, bog gardens

**Origin**  Coast ranges from Santa Clara County north to Butte County, to Alaska. Nevada, New Mexico.

**Comments**  Occasionally has a few short and fertile stems. Can be used to scour pans, flooring, other woodwork. From the Carboniferous Age. Stems are slender and hollow. Perhaps best to grow in a container. There are three species in California. This genus is found all over the world except in Australia and New Zealand. The fertile stem does not branch.

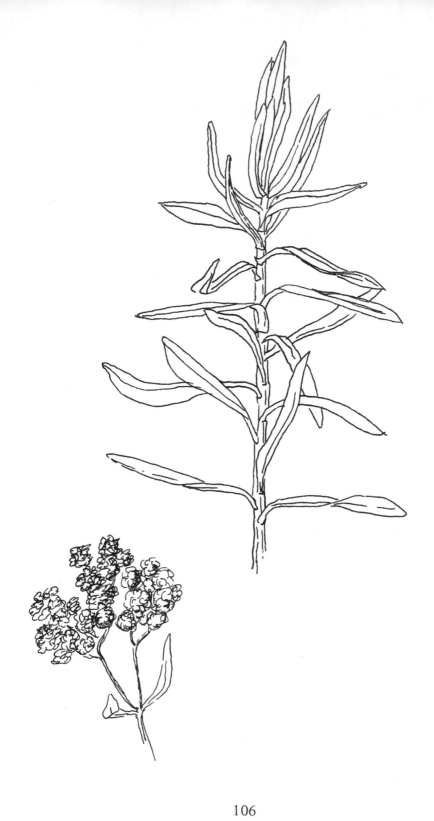

# Eriogonum arborescens

**Common Name**  Santa Cruz Island Buckwheat

**Family**  Polygonaceae

**Leaves**  Evergreen. Whorled. Linear or oblong. Entire, with revolute margins. Grayish above. White tomentose below. ½ to 1½ inches long. One-eighth to one-fourth of an inch wide.

**Flowers**  Whitish to pink. In head-like clusters (cymes) to 6 inches across. Above the foliage. May to September.

**Fruit**  Achene. Dry. October to December.

**Environment**  Full sun. Tolerant to wind. Rocky slopes, canyon walls.

**Pests**  Aster Yellows, Aphids

**Propagation**  Cuttings or seed

**Rate of Growth**  Rapid

**Pruning**  Remove flowers when finished, if desired

**Seasonal Value**  Foliage, flowers

**Shape**  Loosely branched

**Spread**  3½ to 4 feet

**Height**  to 3½ feet

**Soil**  Needs excellent drainage. Tolerant to drought, rocky, dry soils.

**Use**  Specimen, mass planting, on slopes. Effective dry arrangements. Erosion control.

**Origin**  Santa Cruz, Santa Rosa and Anacapa Islands off the coast of southern California.

**Comments**  Attractive to honeybees. Used for medicinal purposes - from stems and the leaves. The trunk and branches have shreddy gray to reddish bark.

# Eriogonum fasciculatum

**Common Name**  California Buckwheat

**Family**  Polygonaceae

**Leaves**  Evergreen. Vary from being green above and white hairy below to grayish-hairy both sides. ½ to ¾ inches long. To ½ inch wide. Fascicled. Revolute. Entire.

**Flowers**  White or pinkish. In compact head-like clusters on long stems. May to October.

**Fruit**  Achene. October to December.

**Environment**  Full sun or partial shade. Best in sun. Dry slopes, canyons near coast.

**Pests**  Aphids

**Propagation**  Cuttings or seed

**Rate of Growth**  Rapid

**Pruning**  Remove dead flowers if desired

**Seasonal Value**  Foliage, flowers

**Shape**  Low, branched

**Spread**  3 to 4 feet

**Height**  2 to 3 feet

**Soil**  Well-drained.

**Use**  Specimen, mass planting, erosion control, for dry slopes.

**Origin**  The foothills of Santa Clara County to San Diego County to Baja California.

**Comments**  Deer do not usually eat this plant. Plants may be variable in appearance. An important bee plant.

# Eriogonum giganteum

**Common Name**  Saint Catherines Lace

**Family**  Polygonaceae

**Leaves**  Evergreen. Alternate. Grayish white. Young leaves especially tomentose. Truncate at base. Prominent veins below. Undulated. Oblong to ovate. To 2½ inches long, to 2 inches wide. Entire.

**Flowers**  Soft grayish. Flower clusters (cymes) twice as large as those of *E. arborescens*. To 12 inches across. Well above the foliage. June to July.

**Fruit**  Achene. October to December.

**Environment**  Full sun. Sunny slopes.

**Pests**  Deer, Aphids

**Propagation**  Seed, cuttings. Sow seeds in flats in late fall or early spring.

**Rate of Growth**  Rapid

**Pruning**  Remove old flowers if desired

**Seasonal Value**  Foliage, flowers

**Shape**  Much-branched

**Spread**  4 to 6 feet

**Height**  3 to 6 feet

**Soil**  Drought-tolerant. Has a long tap root. Needs good drainage.

**Use**  Tall informal hedge. On dry sunny slopes. Effective with other native plants. Dried arrangements. Erosion control.

**Origin**  From the Santa Catalina, San Clemente and Santa Barbara Islands off the coast of southern California.

**Comments**  The trunk has rough, shreddy bark. The young branches are grayish-hairy. Differs from *E. arborescens* in its more freely-branching habit, grayish white coloring, broadly oval - leaves and having a longer period of bloom. Excellent bee plant. Indians used for headaches, stomach pains, eyewash, high blood pressure, etc. Introduced into cultivation about 1900.

# Fragaria chiloensis

**Common Name** Sand Strawberry

**Family** Rosaceae

**Leaves** Evergreen. Palmately compound. With three leaflets. Toothed. Thick. Dark green above. Bluish white, tomentose below. 1 to 1½ inches long (leaflets).

**Flowers** White. In racemes. In clusters of from 1 to 6 flowers. With 5 petals. Yellow center. April to August.

**Fruit** Bright red berries. ½ to ¾ inches in diameter. May to June.

**Environment** Full sun or partial shade. To zero degrees.

**Pests** Crown Borer, Mites, Nematode, Verticillium Wilt, Water Molds, White Flies.

**Propagation** Stolons, division, cuttings

**Rate of Growth** Rapid

**Pruning** Can be cut back severely if needed.

**Seasonal Value** Foliage, flowers, fruit

**Shape** Low, spreading

**Spread** Wide

**Height** 6 to 12 inches

**Soil** Best if light, fertile, well-drained, with organic matter. Deep irrigate frequently. Apply Iron sulfate when chlorotic.

**Use** Ground cover, hanging baskets, wall. Erosion control in sandy soil.

**Origin** On the coast from San Luis Obispo to Alaska. Also in South America.

**Comments** Leaves may become reddish when old and in the winter period. 'Hybrid No. 25' is good for foliage and for fruit. More vigorous. The parent plant introduced into cultivation about 1712. Other native strawberries include F. californica and F. virginiana. Commercial varieties include: 'Donner', 'Lassen', 'Shasta', 'Sierra', 'Tahoe'.

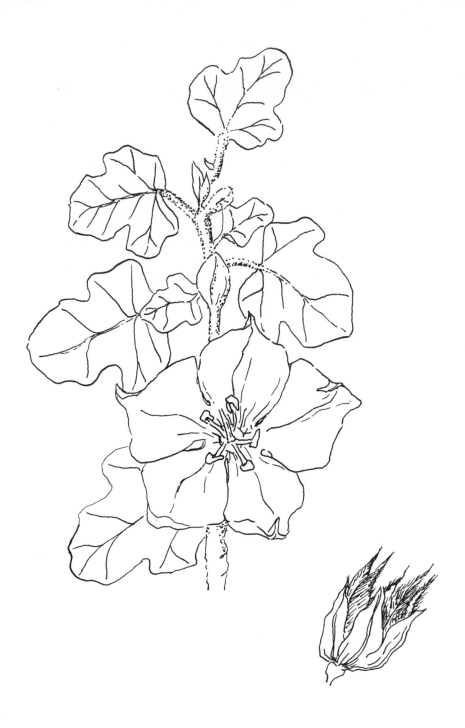

# Fremontodendron californicum

**Common Name**   Common Flannel Bush, Leatherwood, Fremontia

**Family**   Sterculiaceae

**Leaves**   Evergreen. Alternate. Roundish. Entire or palmately 3-lobed. Covered with dense gray or whitish hair below. Short petioles. ½ to 1¼ inches across.

**Flowers**   Lemon yellow. Calyx somewhat flannel-like. Tends to flower all at once - not prolonged. 1½ to 2½ inches across. May to June.

**Fruit**   Ovoid. Capsule. Covered with dense brown hair (bristly). Persistent. Three-fourths to one and one-eighth inches long. Seeds brown and dull.

**Environment**   A hot dry location. Tolerant to drought. Dry slopes from 3000 to 6000 feet. Sea coast conditions.

**Pests**   Greedy Scale, Mealybug

**Propagation**   Seed, cuttings. Soak seed in hot water.

**Rate of Growth**   Rapid

**Pruning**   Thin if necessary. Pinch back when young to prevent legginess.

**Seasonal Value**   Foliage, flowers

**Shape**   Loosely branched

**Spread**   8 to 15 feet

**Height**   6 to 18 feet

**Soil**   Dry, well-drained. Water when young, then discontinue.

**Use**   Specimen. For dry areas, slopes. Erosion control.

**Origin**   Western Sierras from Shasta to Kern Counties to San Diego County and Arizona.

**Comments**   Discovered by General John C. Fremont in 1846. Many species of plants were named for him, but only this genus.

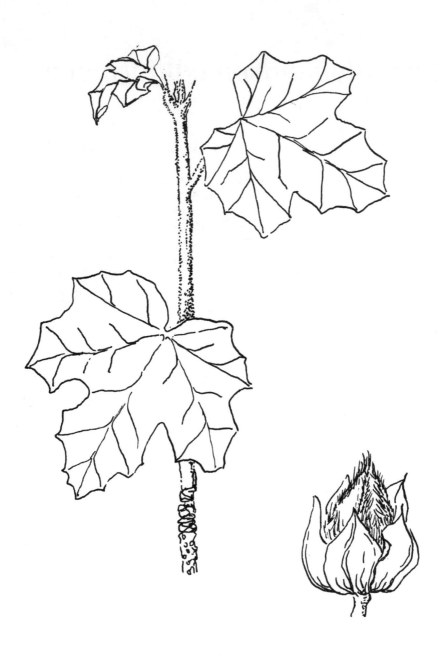

# Fremontodendron mexicanum

**Common Name**  Southern Fremontia

**Family**  Sterculiaceae

**Leaves**  Evergreen. Alternate. Similar to *F. californicum* but usually 3 to 5 lobed. Dark green above. White or rusty hairy below. Leathery. Roundish with stellate hairs. 1¼ to 3 inches across. 5 to 7 main veins from base. Entire.

**Flowers**  Orange-yellow. Reddish at the base on the outside. 1½ to 2½ inches across. Borne along the branches in the leaf axils. 5 stamens. March to May and July to August. Prolonged flowering.

**Fruit**  Conical capsules covered with bristly hairs. Persisting for a long time. Seeds black and shiny. About one-eighth of an inch long.

**Environment**  Full sun in dry areas

**Pests**  Greedy Scale, Mealybug

**Propagation**  Seed, cuttings. To germinate, partially remove hard seed coat by using sand paper, or soak in weak lye solution, or use boiling water.

**Rate of Growth**  Moderate

**Pruning**  Pinch back when young to shape

**Seasonal Value**  Foliage, flowers

**Shape**  More stiff appearing than *F. californicum*

**Spread**  8 to 15 feet

**Height**  8 to 20 feet

**Soil**  Dry, well-drained. Drought-tolerant

**Use**  Specimen. On sunny slopes. Erosion control.

**Origin**  On the dry slopes in the extreme southern area of San Diego County and south into Baja California.

**Comments**  Blooms longer than *F. californicum*. More commonly seen also. *F. mexicanum:* leaves distinctly veined and lobed. Seeds, black, shiny. *F. californicum:* leaves entire to slightly lobed. Seeds brown, dull. In cultivation since 1854. Twigs nutritious for cattle. Inner bark used for making poultices for sores.

# Galvezia speciosa

**Common Name**  Island Bush Snapdragon

**Family**  Scrophulariaceae

**Leaves**  Evergreen. Opposite, or 3 to a node. Oval or oblong. 1 to 1¼ inches long, three-eighths to one-half of an inch wide. Thick and leathery. Entire.

**Flowers**  Borne singly in axils of upper leaves. Forming clusters (racemes) of from 5 to 20 flowers. Scarlet. 1 inch long. February to July. Some flowers all year long. More flowers in the sun.

**Fruit**  August to November. Capsules.

**Environment**  Full sun or partial shade. More shade if in hot area. Rocky canyons.

**Pests**  Aphids

**Propagation**  Seed or cuttings any time (4 to 5 inches long)

**Rate of Growth**  Moderate to rapid

**Pruning**  Prune back occasionally to keep better shape.

**Seasonal Value**  Foliage, flowers

**Shape**  Dense, round

**Spread**  3 to 5 feet

**Height**  7 to 8 feet

**Soil**  Moist soils. Best in good, well-drained soil. Very little water needed after once established.

**Use**  On slopes of rocky canyons. In mixed plantings. On partially shaded slope.

**Origin**  California only on Santa Catalina, San Clemente and Guadalupe Islands.

**Comments**  Two forms. One has hairy leaves, the other is glabrous. The latter is best for the garden. It seems to do best also. Brittle.

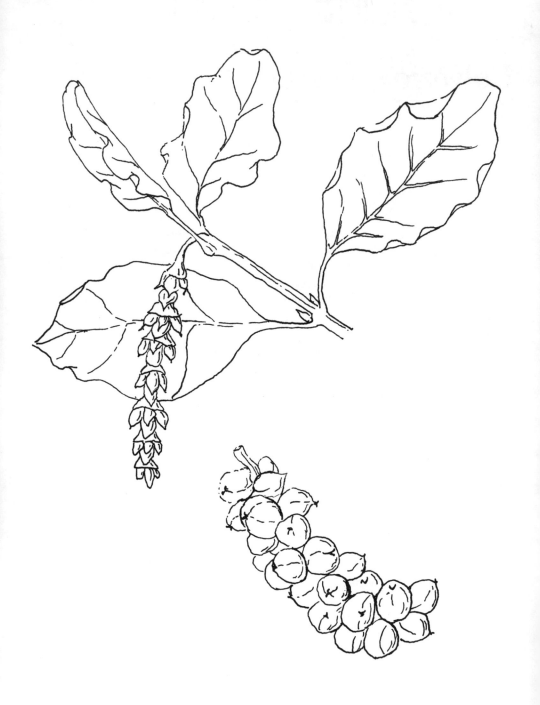

# Garrya elliptica

**Common Name**  Coast Silktassel

**Family**  Garryaceae

**Leaves**  Evergreen. Opposite. Thick and leathery. Elliptic to oval. From 1½ to 2 inches wide. Revolute, undulated. Glabrous above. Tomentose below. 1½ to 2½ inches long. Entire.

**Flowers**  Dioecious. In catkins (racemes). Solitary or clustered. Male is 4 to 7 inches long. Female is 2 to 4 inches long. Male is yellow, female is greenish. January to March.

**Fruit**  Purplish. Globose. Densely white-tomentose. In clusters, like grapes. Each ½ to three-eighths of an inch across. Juicy. August and September.

**Environment**  Full sun or partial shade. Adapted to coastal conditions. Foliage may burn if plant is in too much sun and wind. On dry slopes, ridges below 2000 feet.

**Pests**  Aphids

**Propagation**  Seed, cuttings (softwood). Treat seed in lye solution for 24 hours or stratify 3 months.

**Rate of Growth**  Moderate to rapid

**Pruning**  If needed. Is tolerant.

**Seasonal Value**  Foliage, flowers, fruit

**Shape**  Upright, dense

**Spread**  8 to 10 feet

**Height**  4 to 30 feet

**Soil**  Moist, but with good drainage.

**Use**  Background. Tall screen. Mass effect. Specimen.

**Origin**  Common in the Coast Ranges, especially seaward. From Ventura County to Oregon. Also Santa Cruz Island.

**Comments**  *Garrya elliptica* 'James Roof' has much longer tassels.

# Gaultheria shallon

**Common Name**  Salal

**Family**  Ericaceae

**Leaves**  Evergreen. Alternate. Large, deep green, roundish, glossy. Lighter in the sun. Slightly cordate at the base. Ovate to oblong. Finely toothed. Serrulate. 1¾ to 4 inches long. ¾ to 1½ inches wide.

**Flowers**  White to pinkish. Bell-like. In 6 inch loose clusters. In axillary or terminal racemes. With reddish bracts. Sticky and hairy. March to June.

**Fruit**  Blue-black berries. Edible, though not too tasty. ¼ inch across. With many seeds. June to July. Has a spicy aroma. Birds, livestock eat.

**Environment**  Full sun or partial to much shade. Best in partial shade. To zero degrees. Grows naturally in woods or brush below 2500 feet.

**Pests**  Leaf Spot, Mites, Thrips

**Propagation**  Seed, cuttings, division

**Rate of Growth**  Rapid

**Pruning**  Tolerant to severe pruning, though none may be required.

**Seasonal Value**  Foliage, flowers, fruit.

**Shape**  Variable

**Spread**  wide

**Height**  16 inches in sun, 6 feet in the shade.

**Soil**  Tolerant to poor, dry soil. Best with some moisture. Acid best.

**Use**  Ground cover, banks. Effective under trees, around rocks. Used in floral trade.

**Origin**  From Santa Barbara County north to southern Alaska.

**Comments**  An invasive common shrub in the Redwood belt along the coast from Del Norte County to Monterey County, then northward to British Columbia. Described by botanist David Douglas in 1825. Indians made a syrup from the fruit. Also used for pipes.

# Heteromeles arbutifolia

**Common Name** Toyon, Christmas Berry, California Holly

**Family** Rosaceae

**Leaves** Evergreen. Alternate. Oblong to elliptic. Thick and leathery. Serrate. Dark green and glabrous above. With one main vein from the base. With bristly teeth on the margin. 2 to 4 inches long, ¾ to 1½ inches wide.

**Flowers** White. About three-eighths to one-half of an inch across. In large panicles. Bees like. June to July.

**Fruit** Bright red berries. In clusters. Persisting. Larger at lower elevations. ¼ inch or more across. Birds feed upon the fruit. November to February.

**Environment·** Full sun or partial shade. Grows from sea level to 3500 feet.

**Pests** Many, including Aphids, Snails, Black Scale, Leaf Miner, Leaf Spot, Scab, Fire Blight, etc.

**Propagation** Seed, cuttings. Cuttings in fall or spring.

**Rate of Growth** Rapid

**Pruning** As needed. May encourage more fruit.

**Seasonal Value** Foliage, flowers, fruit

**Shape** Large compact shrub or small tree

**Spread** 5 to 20 feet

**Height** 6 to 10 or 25 feet

**Soil** Best if dry. Will tolerate some summer irrigation.

**Use** Background, screen, slope, erosion control. Used in the florist trade. For winter color.

**Origin** From mountains of southern California to Humboldt County and in the foothills of the Sierra Nevadas from Tulare to Shasta Counties.

**Comments** Berries were used by the Indians. Eaten raw or roasted. They made a beverage from the fruit also. Use the bark and the leaves in a tea for various aches and pains. *H. arbutifolia* 'Macrocarpa' has larger berries.

# Holodiscus discolor

**Common Name** Cream Bush, Ocean Spray

**Family** Rosaceae

**Leaves** Deciduous. Grayish-green. Alternate. Ovate. Entire. Upper half of leaf is serrate. Lower half entire. Soft hairy. To 3 inches long. Three-eighths to two inches wide.

**Flowers** Creamy-white. In pendulous clusters. Numerous. Turning amber in the fall. One-eighth of an inch across. Clusters to 12 inches long. May to July.

**Fruit** Small and hairy. To one-eighth of an inch long.

**Environment** Moist slopes, canyons. Full sun or partial shade.

**Pests** Aphids

**Propagation** Seed, cuttings, suckers

**Rate of Growth** Moderate

**Pruning** If to be pruned, do it after flowers. Remove unsightly pods.

**Seasonal Value** Foliage, flowers

**Shape** Erect or spreading

**Spread** 10 to 12 feet or more

**Height** 3 feet in sun, to 20 feet in shade

**Soil** Rich, moist

**Use** Specimen

**Origin** In the Coast Ranges of California north to British Columbia and in the Sierras. Also east to Rockies.

**Comments** A very desirable plant for the landscape.

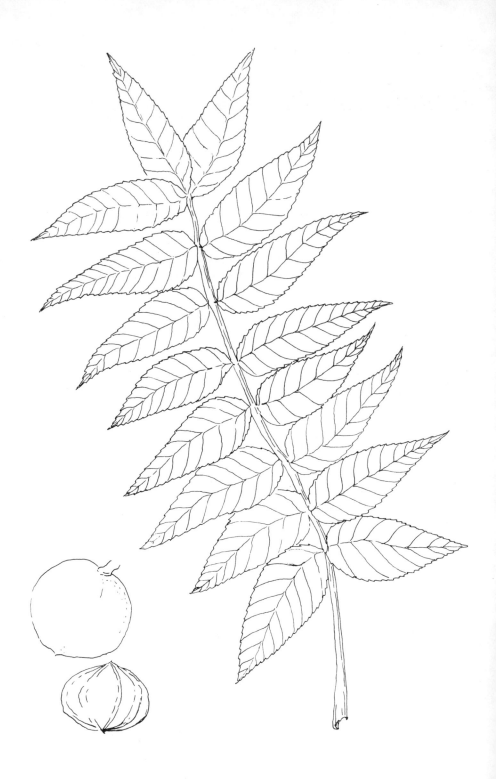

# Juglans hindsii

**Common Name**  California Black Walnut

**Family**  Juglandaceae

**Leaves**  Deciduous. Pinnately compound. Leaves 9 to 14 inches long. Leaflets 15 to 23 and ovate to lanceolate. 2½ to 5 inches long and ¾ to 1½ inches wide. Bright green, glabrous above. Pubescent on main veins below. Serrate.

**Flowers**  Monoecious. Appearing after the leaves. Male flowers in long pendulous catkins. Each flower consisting of 4 to 40 stamens. Female flowers few on short, terminal spikes.

**Fruit**  Mostly smooth nuts. Slightly flattened at ends. Do not split when ripe. Kernel edible. Late fall.

**Environment**  Growing near streams in moist, sandy to gravelly soils. Best in sun. Tolerant to wind, heat. At elevations up to 3000 feet.

**Pests**  Aphids, Codling Moth, Walnut Husk Fly, Walnut Blight, Scales, Mites.

**Propagation**  Seeds, cuttings, suckers

**Rate of Growth**  Moderate to rapid

**Pruning**  Little needed. Will 'bleed' if pruned especially in the early spring.

**Seasonal Value**  Foliage, fruit

**Shape**  Broad, round

**Spread**  20 to 50 feet; Diameter 2 to 3 feet

**Height**  30 to 70 feet

**Soil**  Rich, well-drained best. Tolerant to drought, alkaline soils.

**Use**  Shade, specimen. Rootstock for English Walnut. Wood is excellent for working, though not so valuable as the Eastern Black Walnut.

**Origin**  Central Valley. Lake, Napa to Contra Costa and Stanislaus Counties.

**Comments**  More resistant to excess moisture in root area and to Oak Root Fungus than English Walnut. Has bark that is grayish-brown to black. Furrowed into longitudinal fissures. Is a litter tree. *Juglans californica* is seen in southern California.

# Lithocarpus densiflor*a* ^us^

**Common Name**  Tanbark Oak, Tan Oak

**Family**  Fagaceae

**Leaves**  Evergreen. Alternate. Thick and leathery. Oblong to ovate. Prominent parallel veins. Glabrous or with scattered pubescence above. White or rusty-tomentose below. Dentate. 2 to 5 inches long, ¾ to 2½ inches wide.

**Flowers**  Monoecious. Whitish. June to August.

**Fruit**  An ovoid nut. Maturing the second year. Has a shallow cup at the base, similar to acorns. Fall.

**Environment**  Grows from sea level to 4500 feet. In valleys and low slopes. Near Redwoods (Coast). Tolerant to considerable shade. Best in coastal areas. Not for interior valleys. Part shade.

**Pests**  Aphids, Greedy Scale, Mealybug, Oak Scale, White Fly

**Propagation**  Seed, cuttings

**Rate of Growth**  Moderate to rapid

**Pruning**  When necessary. Shape when young.

**Seasonal Value**  Foliage, flowers, fruit

**Shape**  With ascending branches. Columnar to broad-topped

**Spread**  Wide, to 50 feet

**Height**  50 to 75 or up to 150 feet

**Soil**  Rich, moist, sandy or gravelly best. Tolerant. Good drainage important.

**Use**  Specimen, shade. Bark used for tanning leather. Play areas, etc.

**Origin**  In the coast Ranges from southern California to southwest Oregon.

**Comments**  Bark is thick and furrowed. Young branches are tomentose. Wood is dense and fine-grained. Hard. Could be used for furniture. Often used for firewood. The nuts (acorns) are edible if ground and leached and used for mush, bread, etc.

# Lyonothamnus floribundus var. asplenifolius

**Common Name**  Fernleaf Catalina Ironwood

**Family**  Rosaceae

**Leaves**  Evergreen. Variable. Opposite. Dimorphic. Fernlike. Dark green and glabrous above.  Leaf blades of simple leaves lanceolate and 3 to 6 inches long.  About ½ inch wide.  Nearly entire, or pinnately cut into wedge-shaped lobes. The pinnately compound leaves are 3 to 6 inches long, with 3 to 7 leaflets similar to the simple leaves.

**Flowers**  White. About ¼ inch across. In broad compound terminal clusters. These are 4 to 8 inches across. Fragrant. Summer.

**Fruit**  Brownish, woody capsule. About ¼ inch long. Usually with 4 seeds.

**Environment**  Best in coastal area. Not tolerant to prolonged cold. Neither extremes of heat and cold. Best in full sun. Not for inland valley areas.

**Pests**  Mites, but usually clean

**Propagation**  Seed, cuttings, suckers

**Rate of Growth**  Rapid

**Pruning**  Train to a single trunk when young

**Seasonal Value**  Foliage, flowers, bark

**Shape**  Variable. May be multi-trunked.

**Spread**  15 to 40 feet

**Height**  25 to 50 (80) feet

**Soil**  Should be well-drained. Fertile. Tolerant to some drought. Roots are moderate in depth.

**Use**  Specimen, hedge.

**Origin**  Southern California. Santa Catalina, San Clemente, Santa Rosa, Santa Cruz Islands (Channel Islands).

**Comments**  Will stump sprout. The reddish brown bark peels in long vertical strips. These weather to a silvery gray color. The young twigs are covered with fine hair which later disappears, with the branches becoming bright red.

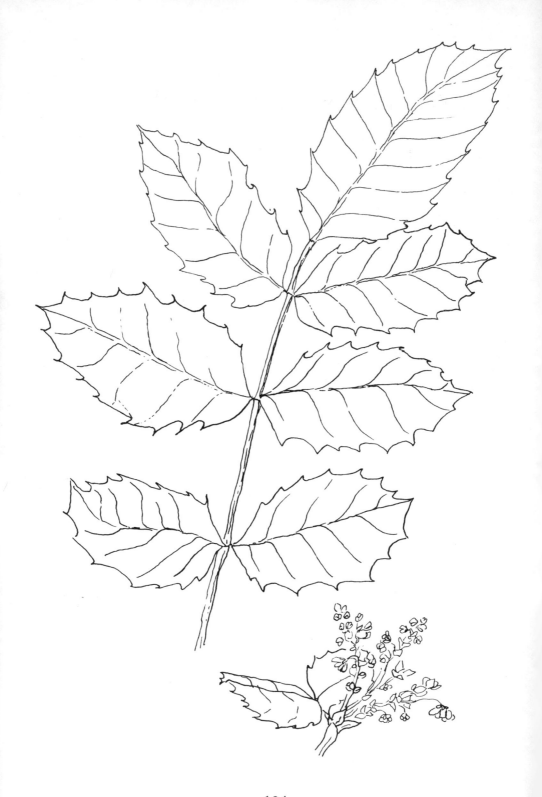

# Mahonia aquifolium

**Common Name**  Oregon Grape

**Family**  Berberidaceae

**Leaves**  Evergreen. Alternate. Odd-pinnately compound. Leaflets 5 to 9. Oblong to ovate. Dark green and glossy above. Spinulose-dentate. Glabrous. Young growth bronzy. Some leaves turning a bright red in fall or when ready to fall off. Leaves 4 to 10 inches long. Leaflets 1½ to 3 inches long.

**Flowers**  Yellow terminal racemes. 2 to 3 inches long. March to May.

**Fruit**  Dark blue. With bloom. Berries edible. For jellies, etc. Birds enjoy. ¼ inch across. May to July.

**Environment**  Best in partial shade. To zero. Wooded slopes below 7000 feet.

**Pests**  Mealybug, Barberry looper (will defoliate)

**Propagation**  Seed, cuttings, suckers, division. Stratify seed 3 months.

**Rate of Growth**  Moderate to rapid

**Pruning**  When necessary. Remove old canes to ground. Encourage new.

**Seasonal Value**  Foliage, flowers, fruit, fall coloring of some leaves

**Shape**  Upright, stiff

**Spread**  1 to 6 feet

**Height**  1 to 6 feet

**Soil**  Well-drained. Deep roots. Tolerant to summer water. Spreading by rhizomes.

**Use**  Shade plant. Group planting, barrier, containers.

**Origin**  Humboldt and Trinity Counties to Modoc County north to Oregon, Washington, British Columbia.

**Comments**  Several cultivars available. Fruit have been used to make a beverage. Sometimes have been dried by Indians for winter use. Roots, stems used for a yellow dye, for baskets, fabrics, etc. Various parts used for medicinal purposes. Cultivar 'Compacta'.

# Mahonia nervosa

**Common Name**  Longleaf Mahonia

**Family**  Berberidaceae

**Leaves**  Evergreen. Bristly toothed. Clustered at ends of stems. Glossy green. Leaflets ovate to lanceolate. Serrulate, with 6 to 12 bristly teeth on each side. Some red leaves during cold weather. Leaves pinnately compound and from 8 to 18 inches long. 11 to 23 leaflets and each from 1 to 3¾ inches long and to 1¾ inches wide. Alternate.

**Flowers**  Yellow. In erect racemes which are 3 to 6 inches long. April to June.

**Fruit**  Blue. Glaucous. In clusters. Each berry one-quarter to one-third of an inch across. July to August.

**Environment**  Best in partial shade. Shaded slopes below 6000 feet.

**Pests**  Caterpillars, snails, slugs

**Propagation**  Cuttings, seed, division. Stratify seed 2 to 3 months.

**Rate of Growth**  Rapid

**Pruning**  Cut old stems to ground when needed

**Seasonal Value**  Foliage, flowers, fruit, fall coloring

**Shape**  Low shrub. Upright

**Spread**  To 2 feet

**Height**  ¾ to 2 feet, rarely to 6 feet

**Soil**  Tolerant to summer water. Best with some moisture. Spreading by rhizomes.

**Use**  Under Oaks, Pines, Madrones, etc. Low barrier, ground cover.

**Origin**  In the forests from British Columbia south to Washington, Oregon, California down to Monterey and San Benito Counties. Also in Shasta, Siskiyou and Trinity Counties. In the Blue Mountains of Oregon and Idaho.

**Comments**  Bark used for dyes. Fruit used for jellies, etc.

# *Mahonia nevinii*

**Common Name**  Nevins Barberry

**Family**  Berberidaceae

**Leaves**  Evergreen  Alternate. Often in small clusters.  1½ to 3 inches long. Pinnately compound, with 3 to 7 leaflets.  The terminal leaflet 1 to 1½ inches long.  Others ¾ inch long.  Lanceolate to ovate.  Bristly margins. New growth bronzy, then becoming a grayish-green when mature.

**Flowers**  In short loose racemes at ends of branches.  1 to 2 inches long.  5 to 9 flowers each cluster.  Each flower ¼ inch across.  Yellow.  March to May.

**Fruit**  Translucent yellowish-red berries.  ½ inch across.  June to July.

**Environment**  Best in sun.  Below 2000 feet.

**Pests**  Caterpillars, slugs, snails

**Propagation**  Seed, cuttings, division.  Stratify seed 3 months.

**Rate of Growth**  Moderate

**Pruning**  Cut old branches to ground when necessary

**Seasonal Value**  Foliage, flowers, fruit, fall coloring

**Shape**  Upright, stiff

**Spread**  3 to 10 feet

**Height**  3 to 10 feet

**Soil**  Tolerant to any soil, excess water, deficient water. Best if sandy or gravelly .

**Use**  Specimen, screen, hedge, ground cover, barrier

**Origin**  In Los Angeles, Riverside, San Bernardino and San Diego Counties.

**Comments**  Introduced into cultivation about 1882.

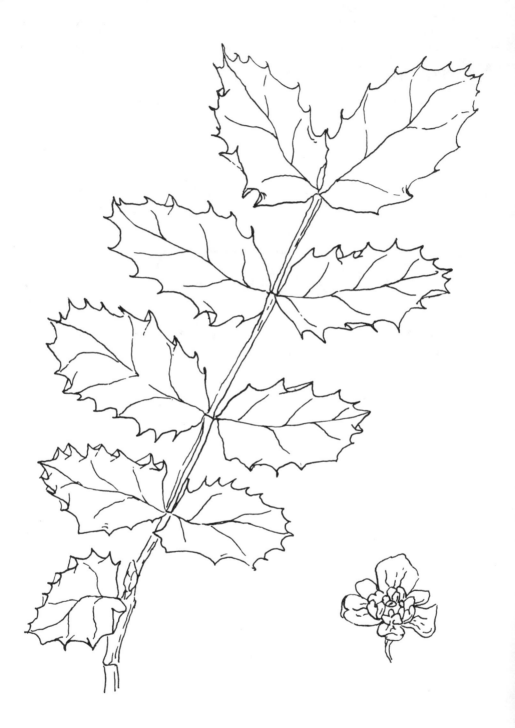

# *Mahonia pinnata*

**Common Name**  California Holly Grape

**Family**  Berberidaceae

**Leaves**  Evergreen. Alternate. Pinnately compound. Spiny-toothed. 5 to 12 inches long. Usually 5 to 9 leaflets and crowded to over-lapping, ovate to oblong. 1 to 2¼ inches long.

**Flowers**  Yellow. In terminal racemes. March to May.

**Fruit**  Blue. Glaucous. ¼ inch across. July and August.

**Environment**  Tolerant to heat, drought. Full sun. Below 4000 feet.

**Pests**  Caterpillars, Slugs, Snails, Mealybugs

**Propagation**  Seed, cuttings, division. Stratify seed 3 months.

**Rate of Growth**  Moderate

**Pruning**  Cut old branches to ground when needed

**Seasonal Value**  Foliage, flowers, fruit, fall coloring

**Shape**  Stiff, upright

**Spread**  5 feet or more

**Height**  2½ feet or more

**Soil**  Tolerant. Spreads by Rhizomes.

**Use**  Specimen, ground cover, container, barrier

**Origin**  Coast Ranges, Lower California, San Diego, Los Angeles Counties, north to southern Oregon.

**Comments**  Similar to Oregon Grape, but more crinkly. Bark and roots used for a dye and for medicinal purposes. Cultivar 'Ken Hartman'.

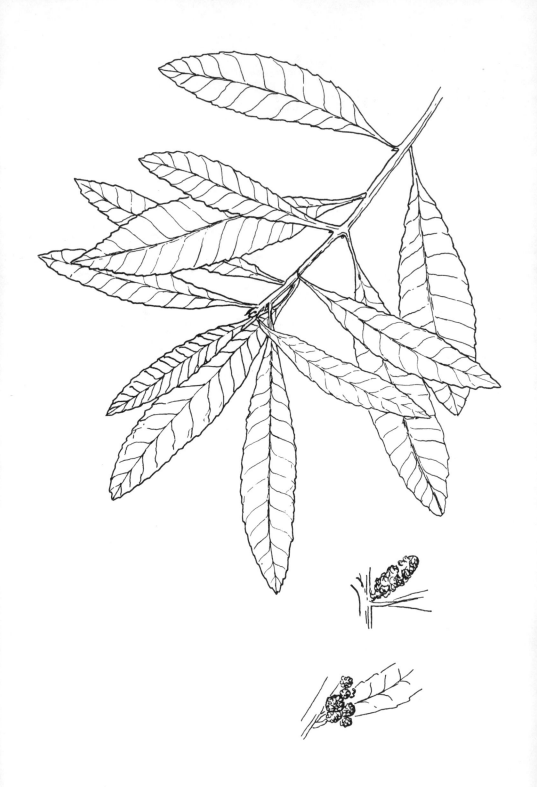

# Myrica californica

**Common Name**  Pacific Wax Myrtle

**Family**  Myricaceae

**Leaves**  Evergreen. Dark green. Glossy. Oblong to oblanceolate. Acute. Entire or finely serrate. Resinous dotted on the under side. Aromatic. Alternate. 2 to 4½ inches long, ½ to ¾ inch wide.

**Flowers**  White. Rather small. In catkins. March to May.

**Fruit**  Purplish. Glaucous. Round. ¼ inch across. Birds and squirrels enjoy. July to September.

**Environment**  Full sun, partial shade. Does well in coastal regions, not interior valleys. In sand dunes, flats with moisture, Redwood slopes.

**Pests**  Mites, Thrips

**Propagation**  Seed, cuttings. Stratify seed for 3 months

**Rate of Growth**  Moderate to slow

**Pruning**  Tolerant to pruning, but exudes much sap when cut.

**Seasonal Value**  Foliage, fruit

**Shape**  Large compact shrub or small tree

**Spread**  15 to 20 feet

**Height**  10 to 35 feet

**Soil**  Moist, rich, with sufficient organic matter. Irrigate in summer

**Use**  Specimen, informal hedge. Along streams, in groves.

**Origin**  Santa Monica Mountains to Santa Cruz Mountains and Del Norte County north to Washington.

**Comments**  Has a grayish bark. Introduced into cultivation in 1849. Grows low, flat at beach. Young branches are hairy. Below 500 feet.

# Physocarpus capitatus

**Common Name**  Ninebark

**Family**  Rosaceae

**Leaves**  Deciduous. Alternate. Petioled. Palmately 3 to 5 lobed. Round to ovate. Lobes serrate. Mostly glabrous. 2 to 4 inches long and as wide. New growth pubescent.

**Flowers**  White. In terminal corymbs or umbels. April to July.

**Fruit**  Inflated reddish-brown capsule. July to August.

**Environment**  On moist banks, north slopes below 4500 feet. Part shade.

**Pests**  Aphids

**Propagation**  Seed, cuttings

**Rate of Growth**  Moderate to rapid

**Pruning**  As needed

**Seasonal Value**  Foliage, flowers

**Shape**  Erect or spreading

**Spread**  6 to 8 feet

**Height**  6 to 8 feet

**Soil**  Tolerant. But best if moist and with sufficient organic matter.

**Use**  Specimen

**Origin**  Coast Ranges from Santa Barbara County to British Columbia and in the Sierras from Tulare County north.

**Comments**  Bark exfoliates in narrow strips.

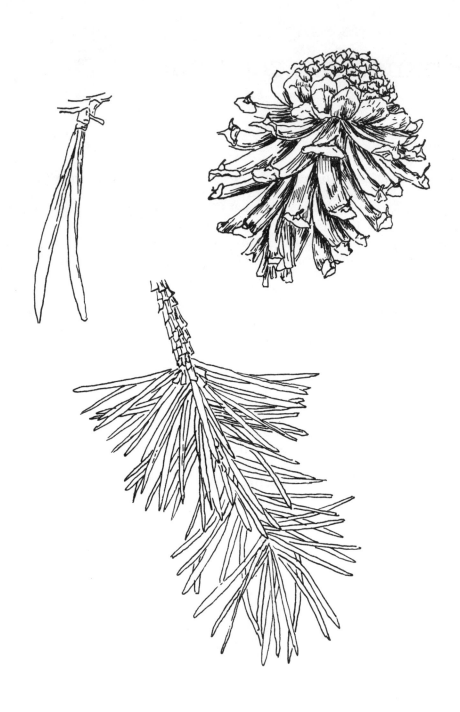

# *Pinus contorta*

**Common Name**  Shore Pine, Beach Pine

**Family**  Pinaceae

**Leaves**  Evergreen. In bundles of two. Stout, often twisted. Dark green. 1 to 3 inches long. Persisting for 4 to 6 years.

**Flowers**  Male: short crowned spikes; Female: clusters or pairs on short stout stems. Orange to red in color.

**Fruit**  Ovoid cones. ¾ to 2½ inches long. With prickly scales. Remaining closed on tree for many years.

**Environment**  Usually grows below 5000 feet. On high plateaus, benches.

**Pests**  Aphids

**Propagation**  Seed, cuttings. Stratify seed 3 months.

**Rate of Growth**  Slow

**Pruning**  Only as needed

**Seasonal Value**  Foliage, cones

**Shape**  Round top

**Spread**  15 to 30 feet, to 18 inches in diameter

**Height**  15 to 30 feet

**Soil**  Best in sandy, moist soils. Will tolerate dry gravelly soils.

**Use**  Mine timbers, pulp, fuel, ties, poles, posts

**Origin**  Mendocino and Humboldt Counties, and up the coast of Alaska.

**Comments**  Bark is ¾ to 1 inch thick, divided by fissures in both directions.

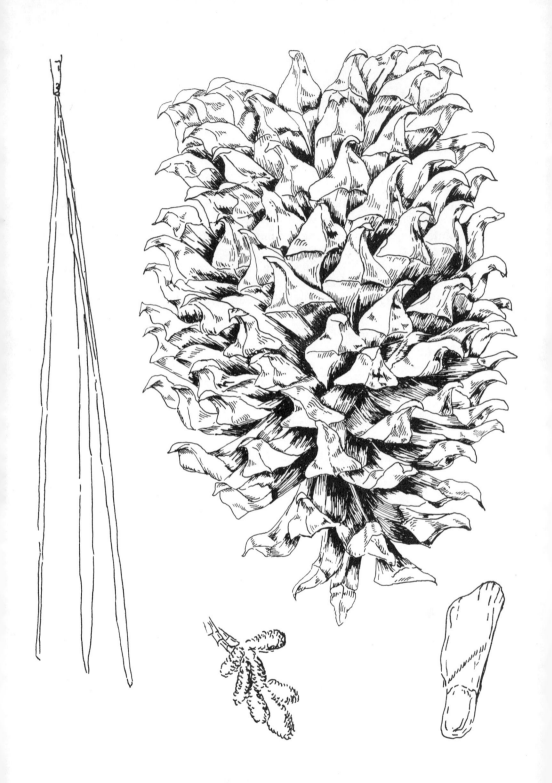

# Pinus coulteri

**Common Name**  Coulter Pine

**Family**  Pinaceae

**Leaves**  Evergreen. In bundles of three. With sharp points. Stiff, heavy, straight. Deep or bluish-green. 5 to 12 inches long - usually about 9 inches.

**Flowers**  Male: yellow; Female: dark reddish-brown. May and June.

**Fruit**  Yellowish-brown cones. Heavily armed. Larger and heavier than the cones of any other Pine. Broadly ovoid. From 9 to 14 inches long. Maturing by August of the second summer. Cones open in October.

**Environment**  On warm dry slopes and ridges. Never in a pure forest. From 15 to 100 degrees range. Tolerant to heat, drought, wind, desert conditions. Best in full sun. Occurring from 1000 to 6000 feet.

**Pests**  Aphids

**Propagation**  Seed, cuttings

**Rate of Growth**  Moderate

**Pruning**  Only if necessary

**Seasonal Value**  Foliage, cones

**Shape**  Open. Trunk not branched.

**Spread**  20 to 40 feet, 1½ to 2½ feet in diameter

**Height**  40 to 80 feet

**Soil**  Dry, gravelly soils

**Use**  Erosion control. Rarely cut, but suitable for second-grade lumber. Wood is light, soft, coarse-grained, reddish-brown.

**Origin**  Mt. Diablo, Mt. Hamilton, Santa Lucia Ranges and mountains of southern California south to Baja California.

**Comments**  Large lower branches are long, bending downward even to the soil level, with an upward curve at the tips. Bark is rough and furrowed and ridged. A dark or blackish-brown. Trees bear when tree is 20 to 30 years old. Cones break at base when falling, leaving a few scales on each branch. Seeds are one-half to two-thirds of an inch long and winged. Wings about one inch long. Each cone has from 9 to 12 seeds.

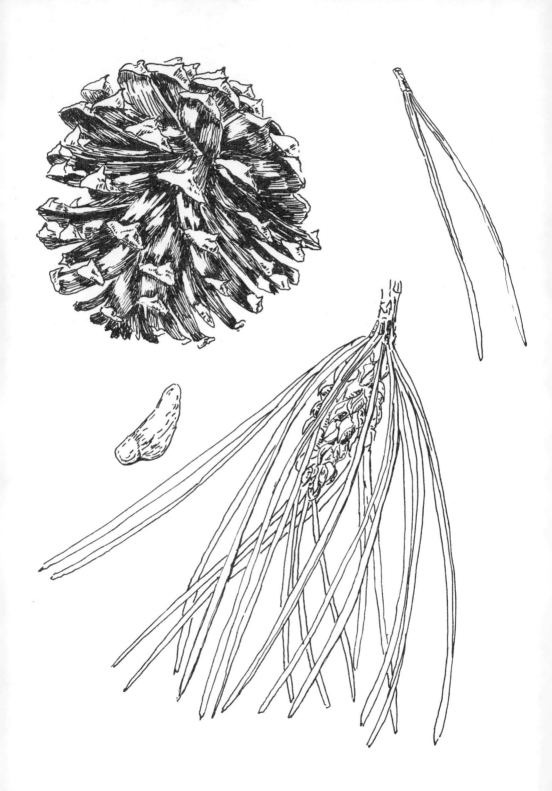

# Pinus muricata

**Common Name**  Bishop Pine

**Family**  Pinaceae

**Leaves**  Evergreen. In bundles of two. Long and rigid. Usually twisted. Yellowish-green. 4 to 6 inches long.

**Flowers**  March to April

**Fruit**  Cones which are ovoid and oblique. 2 to 3½ inches long and about as wide. Roundish when mature. Borne in circles of 3 to 5. Scales terminating in sharp prickles or curved spurs.

**Environment**  Always found within 2 miles of the coast. Tolerant to wind and salt air. From 20 to 95 degrees. Full sun.

**Pests**  Aphids

**Propagation**  Seed, cuttings Stratify seed 2 months.

**Rate of Growth**  Moderate to rapid

**Pruning**  Only if needed

**Seasonal Value**  Foliage, cones

**Shape**  Round or flat top. More compact when young

**Spread**  20 to 40 feet, 15 to 20 inch diameter

**Height**  45 to 75 feet

**Soil**  Tolerant to poor soil, moisture.

**Use**  Windbreak. For bridge timbers, fuel, Christmas Trees

**Origin**  Coastal regions of Humboldt, Mendocino, Sonoma, Marin, Monterey, San Luis Obispo, Santa Barbara Counties and Lower California.

**Comments**  Bark is rough and furrowed. Wood is heavy and strong. Cones opened by fire, seed then germinates more easily. Many are seen on the Point Reyes Peninsula and along the Sonoma Coast.

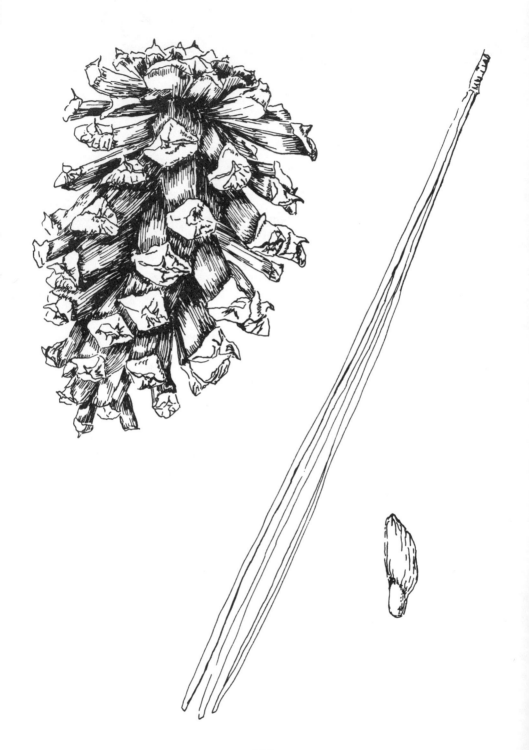

# Pinus ponderosa

**Common Name**  Ponderosa Pine, Western Yellow Pine

**Family**  Pinaceae

**Leaves**  Evergreen. In bundles of 3, sometimes 2. Glossy-yellow-green to dark green. Stiff. In clusters at ends of branches. 4 to 11 inches long.

**Flowers**  Male: short compact clusters, yellow; Female: red. May and June.

**Fruit**  Cones. 3 to 5 inches long. Light to reddish-brown. Prickly scales. Oblong to ovoid. Breaking through the base when falling. A few scales are left on the tree. Seeds one-quarter to one-third of an inch long. Wing to one inch. May and June.

**Environment**  Full sun for best growth. Hardy but not good in desert heat and wind. From sea level to 9000 feet. From 28 to 110 degrees. Best on west slopes.

**Pests**  Mistletoe. Bark Beetles, Red Ring Rot, Cottony Root Rot, Pandora Moth, Squirrels, Porcupines, etc.

**Propagation**  Seed, cuttings. Stratify seed 1 month.

**Rate of Growth**  Moderate to rapid (50 feet in 50 years)

**Pruning**  Only as needed

**Seasonal Value**  Foliage, cones

**Shape**  Stately. With a straight trunk. Massive.

**Spread**  30 to 40 feet, diameter to 8 feet

**Height**  50 or 60 or to 200 feet.

**Soil**  Does well on dry, sandy soil, but is quite tolerant. Requires some moisture. Acid soil best, but tolerant to some alkali.

**Use**  An excellent timber tree. Second in importance to Douglas Fir. The most prevalent Pine in the West. Pitch is adhesive. Indians used on canoes, tents. For Christmas trees, containers, Bonsai, specimen.

**Origin**  From British Columbia to Mexico, including California, East to Nebraska, Texas, Oklahoma. Is the state tree of Montana.

**Comments**  Wood is variable in color. From pale lemon-yellow to an orange-brown or reddish-yellow. Rather light and fine-grained. Bark is yellowish-brown. Fissured into rounded ridges or on old trees into large smooth or scaly plants. Cinnamon-red. Bark flakes are yellow on the inside. On Jeffrey Pine they are gray and smell like Pineapple. Ponderosa smells like Vanilla. Covers a wider range than any other American cone-bearing tree. Lives to 350 to 500 years or more.

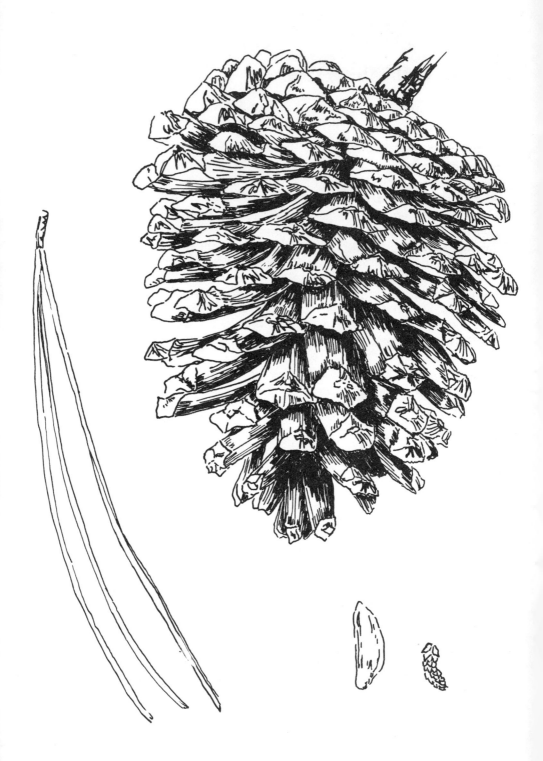

# Pinus radiata

**Common Name**  Monterey Pine

**Family**  Pinaceae

**Leaves**  Evergreen. In bundles of 3. Rarely in twos. 3½ to 6 inches long. A bright green when tree is young. May be bluish-green on mature trees. Densely crowded on the branches. Persisting for 4 years.

**Flowers**  In late winter or early spring.

**Fruit**  Broad, asymmetrical cones. Grayish. From 2 to 5 inches long. In clusters of 3 to 7. Persisting on the tree for many years. Outer cone scales thickened and rounded. Seeds ¼ inch long. No prickles.

**Environment**  Full sun best. Tolerant to partial shade. Tolerant to heat and cold, wind, salt spray. Wide climatic adaptability, but best in cool, coastal areas. Growing much larger in deep, fertile soils. To 15 degrees.

**Pests**  Many, including Aphids, Mites, Pine Tip Borer, Pine Tip Moth, Pine Leaf Scale, Irregular Pine Scale, Monterey Pine Scale. Western Gall Rust.

**Propagation**  Seed, cuttings

**Rate of Growth**  Most rapid of over 90 species of Pines in the world. Is slower-growing where climate is cold.

**Pruning**  Only as needed

**Seasonal Value**  Foliage, cones

**Shape**  Compact, pyramidal, and becoming more variable with maturity

**Spread**  30 to 50 feet

**Height**  40 to 80 (100) feet

**Soil**  Tolerant. But best in light, well-drained, sandy soil. Tolerant to drought. Roots not usually deep. Down to about 2 feet. Usually found in top 12 inches of soil. Strong lateral root system.

**Use**  Windbreak, erosion control, Christmas tree, hedge, etc. In Australia, New Zealand, Chile, Spain, South Africa it becomes an important pulp and lumber tree.

**Origin**  Three localities on the central coast: Monterey Peninsula, Cambria, and north of Cambria (at Pico Creek). Below 1000 feet.

**Comments**  Noted for its wind configuration on the coast. Trunk is almost black, deeply furrowed bark. May be covered with 'Spanish Moss' - actually a lichen, *Romalina reticulata* - which gives the woods a grayish appearance. Average life is 80 to 90 years. Wide variety in growth rate, form, wood density, branching habit, cone abundance. Grows 12 inches in one year. 3 to 6 feet in 3 years.

# Pinus sabiniana

**Common Name**   Digger Pine

**Family**   Pinaceae

**Leaves**   Evergreen. In bundles of 3. Stiff, wiry. 7 to 13 inches long. Grayish-green. Stand out at angles so the tree casts very little shade. Have a sheen which reflects sunlight. Comparatively slender, usually drooping at the ends of the branchlets.

**Flowers**   April and May

**Fruit**   Light, chocolate-brown cones which are broadly ovoid. 6 to 10 inches long. Scales tipped by sharp, stout, often hooked spurs. Seed is ¾ inch long, with a short wing from ¼ to ½ inch long.

**Environment**   On arid, lower slopes of the Coast Ranges and the Sierras, North and Central California from 100 to 3000 feet - in hot, dry valleys and foothills. To 10 degrees. Full sun.

**Pests**   Aphids

**Propagation**   Seed, cuttings

**Rate of Growth**   Rapid. Much faster in rich, moist soil.

**Pruning**   Only as needed

**Seasonal Value**   Foliage, cones

**Shape**   Rounded, or pyramidal when young. When mature, developing a u-shaped fork near the tree top.

**Spread**   25 to 30 feet

**Height**   40 to 80 feet

**Soil**   Does well in dry, shallow, coarse, gravelly soils. Needs little water.

**Use**   Specimen. Windbreak, erosion control. An important food tree for the Digger Indians years ago. Next to the Coulter Pine, produces the heaviest and largest cone of all American Pines.

**Origin**   From southern California along the Coast Ranges to Contra Costa County. See above.

**Comments**   Bark is a dark gray, roughly and irregularly fissured. Does not grow in pure forests. Best growth between 2000 and 3000 feet. Wood is very coarse-grained, dark yellowish-brown, often tinged with red. Locally the Pine Nuts are used for food.

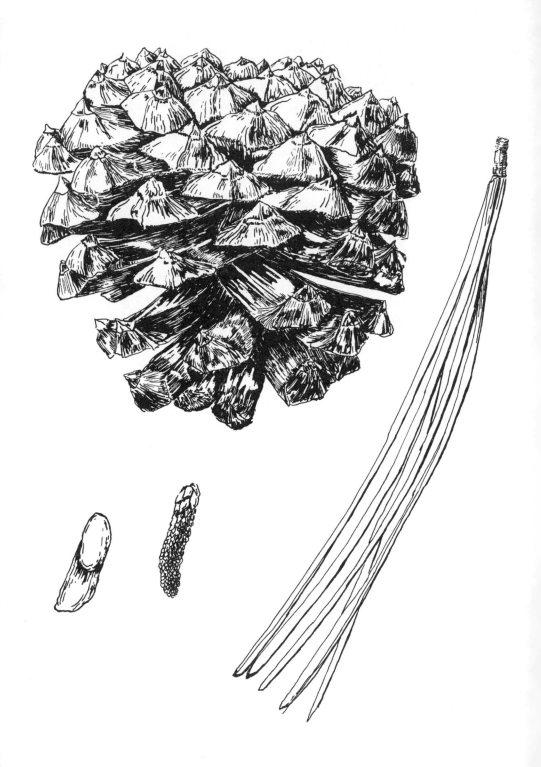

# *Pinus torreyana*

**Common Name**  Torrey Pine, Soledad Pine

**Family**  Pinaceae

**Leaves**  In bundles of five. A dark grayish-green. In terminal clusters. Stiff. Triangular in cross-section. Each surface with visible stomata. Remaining on tree 3 to 4 years. 7 to 12 inches long.

**Flowers**  Male flowers yellow. In short dense heads.

**Fruit**  Cones a chocolate-brown color. Broadly ovoid. Strongly attached. Tips of scales triangular at apex. Part of cone remains on tree. Good cone-production after 15 to 18 years. 4 to 6 inches long. Seeds edible.

**Environment**  Full sun. Temperature range of from 25 to 95 degrees and where the average rainfall is about 15 inches per year. Growing on the coast where exposed to wind and fog. Below 500 feet.

**Pests**  Aphids

**Propagation**  Seed, cuttings

**Rate of Growth**  Moderate

**Pruning**  Only if needed

**Seasonal Value**  Foliage, cones

**Shape**  Somewhat distorted in native habitat

**Spread**  25 to 30 feet

**Height**  20 to 40 or to 60 feet or more

**Soil**  Best if dry, well-drained. Occurs in an area comprised of decomposed sandstone.

**Use**  Specimen. For parks and other large areas

**Origin**  Endemic to Santa Rosa Island and to a confined area in San Diego County, about a mile in width and on both sides of the Soledad River, north of Del Mar.

**Comments**  In its natural habitat, this tree is shorter in height, somewhat distorted. The maximum height here may be about 35 feet, and with a trunk diameter of 8 to 14 inches. The bark of the young tree and of the branches is thick, spongy and a dull gray color. At maturity, the trunk is about one inch thick. It is comprised of ridges, with wide, light reddish-brown scales. The wood is soft, brittle and coarsely-grained. It is a pale reddish-brown color. Away from its native area, the tree can be more upright and much taller.

# *Platanus racemosa*

**Common Name**  Western Sycamore

**Family**  Platanaceae

**Leaves**  Deciduous. Alternate. Palmately lobed. 3 to 5 lobes to or below the middle. 5 to 10 (18) inches across. To 12 inches long. Lobes longer than wide. Entire, or tipped with hardened swellings. Light green and glabrous above. Hairy below. Petioles ½ to 3 inches long. With conspicuous stipules which persist after leaf fall.

**Flowers**  Greenish. In dense heads (globular clusters). February to April.

**Fruit**  One-seeded nutlet covered with long hairs. ¾ to 1 inch in diameter. Persisting. An achene.

**Environment**  Full sun. Tolerant to heat, cold. Adaptable. Below 4000 feet.

**Pests**  Sycamore Anthracnose (Blight), Mildew, Mites, Sycamore Scale.

**Propagation**  Seed, cuttings. Stratify seed 2 to 3 months.

**Rate of Growth**  Rapid

**Pruning**  Tolerant. As needed.

**Seasonal Value**  Foliage, bark

**Shape**  Variable. Round top. Often multiple-trunked

**Spread**  50 to 70 feet

**Height**  40 to 90 feet

**Soil**  Tolerant. Best in deep, rich, moist soil. Tolerant to alkali. Has a shallow, spreading root system.

**Use**  Erosion control, shade.

**Origin**  Along the streams in California foothills and in the Coast Ranges.

**Comments**  Has brittle branches. Hairs may be irritating to some people. Lobes are longer and more pointed than the London Plane Tree and others. Bark is palish or whitish and it exfoliates in thin plates. Susceptibility to Anthracnose precludes general use of this tree in the landscape.

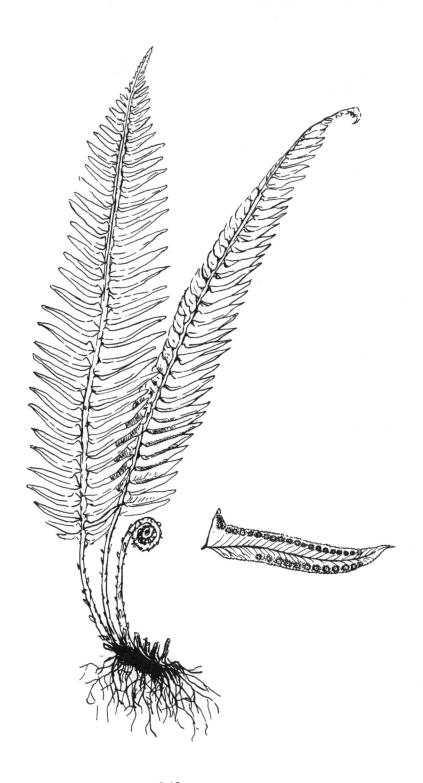

# *Polystichum munitum*

**Common Name**  Western Sword Fern

**Family**  Polypodiaceae

**Leaves**  An herbaceous perennial.  It has fronds that are coarse and from 2 to 5 feet in length.  Where each pinna is attached to the midrib, there is a projection resembling the hilt of a sword.  Fronds taper to a sharp point.  Margins are sharply toothed.  Fronds may number 75 to 100.  Stems are from 2 to 20 inches long.  Fronds are pinnate.

**Flowers**  None

**Fruit**  Sori (Spore Cases) are reddish-brown in color.  Are on underside of fronds, on the veins.

**Environment**  Partial shade.  In damp woods.  Mostly below 2500 feet.

**Pests**  Mites, Foliar Nematode

**Propagation**  Spores, division

**Rate of Growth**  Rapid

**Pruning**  Remove injured fronds

**Seasonal Value**  Foliage

**Shape**  Round mound

**Spread**  2 to 4 feet

**Height**  2 to 4 feet

**Soil**  Rich, with sufficient organic matter and moisture

**Use**  Ground cover.  For rock gardens and shade gardens.

**Origin**  In forest areas near the coast from Monterey County to Del Norte County.  To Alaska, Montana.  On Santa Cruz Island.

**Comments**  For best appearance in the landscape, remove old fronds periodically.

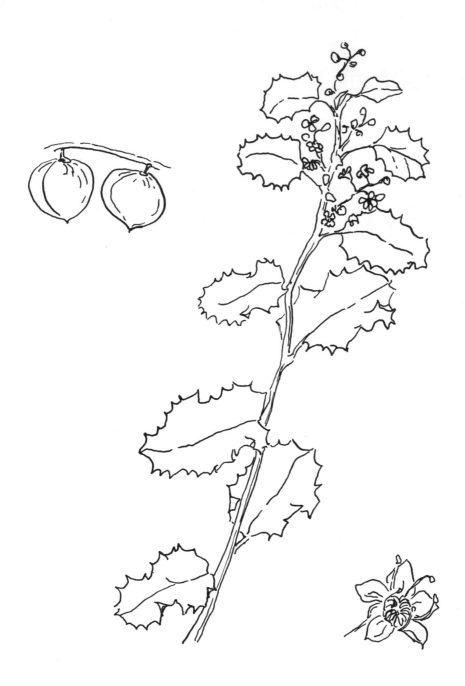

# Prunus ilicifolia

**Common Name**  Hollyleaf Cherry

**Family**  Rosaceae

**Leaves**  Evergreen. Alternate. Spinosely-toothed. Undulated. Dark green and glossy. New foliage much lighter green. Mature leaves thick and leathery. Ovate to elliptic. 1 to 2 inches long, 1 to 1½ inches wide.

**Flowers**  Creamy-white. In short-peduncled racemes. Individual flowers about ½ inch across. Racemes 1 to 2 inches long. Appearing with, or just before the new leaves. April to May.

**Fruit**  Reddish, dark purple or black drupe. Edible and sweet. July to October. Has an after-taste.

**Environment**  Full sun or partial shade. Tolerant to desert or seacoast conditions. Not prolonged freezing. Best in sun. To 10 degrees.

**Pests**  Caterpillars, White Flies. Resistant to Oak Root Fungus

**Propagation**  Seed, cuttings. Seed directly in soil.

**Rate of Growth**  Rapid

**Pruning**  Thin only if necessary. Tolerant to severe cutting.

**Seasonal Value**  Foliage, flowers, fruit

**Shape**  Dense large shrub or small tree

**Spread**  10 to 25 feet

**Height**  10 to 25 feet

**Soil**  Tolerant. Tolerant to drought. Best if well-drained. Roots average to deep. Occasional irrigation only.

**Use**  Background, hedge, screen

**Origin**  Coast Ranges from Napa and Solano Counties south to the mountains of southern and Baja California.

**Comments**  Reseeds prolifically. Bark is smooth and a dark gray color. May be a litter plant, with the seedlings, and the flowers. *Prunus lyoni* is larger than this plant. Fruit is eaten and the seeds have been ground into a meal used for porridge, soup. Wood is heavy and fine-grained. These trees are long-lived. Hybridizes with *Prunus lyonii.*

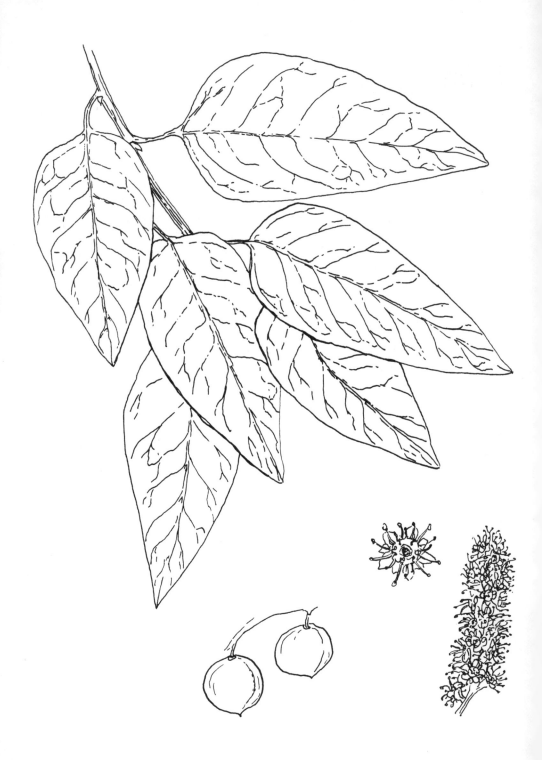

# *Prunus lyonii*

**Common Name**  Catalina Cherry

**Family**  Rosaceae

**Leaves**  Evergreen. Alternate. Thick and leathery. Broadly ovate or oblong to lanceolate. Dark green and glabrous above. Entire or nearly so. Petioles one-eighth to one-half an inch long. 2½ to 5 inches long, 1 to 2½ inches wide.

**Flowers**  White. Each about ¼ inch across. In dense racemes that are 3 to 5 inches long, each with 20 to 40 flowers. March to June.

**Fruit**  Dark purple to black drupe. Aftertaste, but edible. About one inch in diameter. July to October

**Environment**  Full sun, partial shade. Best in sun.

**Pests**  Moth larvae, White Fly. Resistant to Oak Root fungus.

**Propagation**  Seed, cuttings. Seed directly in soil.

**Rate of Growth**  Rapid

**Pruning**  As needed. Tolerant to severe cutting

**Seasonal Value**  Foliage, flowers, fruit

**Shape**  Variable, a large shrub or small tree

**Spread**  15 to 30 feet

**Height**  15 to 45 feet

**Soil**  Tolerant, but best on dry side. Good drainage. Summer water until established.

**Use**  Specimen, screen, hedge

**Origin**  On the islands - Santa Catalina, San Clemente, Santa Cruz.

**Comments**  The racemes are longer than those of *Prunus ilicifolia*. Also easier to train as a tree. Is a litter plant. Self-hybridizes with *P. ilicifolia*.

# *Pseudotsuga menziesii*

**Common Name**  Douglas Fir

**Family**  Pinaceae

**Leaves**  Evergreen. Short, flat and linear. Aromatic. Bluish-green above. With two grayish bands below. Petioles twisted. Densely arranged on the branches. Persisting for 5 to 8 years. ¾ to 1½ inches long, one-sixteenth of an inch wide.

**Flowers**  Male flowers yellow

**Fruit**  Reddish-brown, ovoid cones. With conspicuous narrow 3-pointed bracts. Pendulous. 1½ to 3½ inches long. Fall and winter.

**Environment**  Full sun, partial shade. Best in humid environment. Tolerant to wind (moderate). Moist slopes below 5000 feet.

**Pests**  Aphids, Mites

**Propagation**  Seed, cuttings. Stratify seed 2 months.

**Rate of Growth**  Rapid

**Pruning**  When young, to make more compact

**Seasonal Value**  Foliage, fruit

**Shape**  Pyramidal, with long drooping branches

**Spread**  30 to 60 feet

**Height**  70 to 250 to 300 feet

**Soil**  Tolerant, but with good drainage. Roots are deep and spreading.

**Use**  Specimen, hedge, windbreak, Christmas tree, lumber

**Origin**  Mountains of western United States, including the Pacific Coast, Mexico, British Columbia and the Rocky Mountain region. Coast ranges from Monterey County north. Sierra Nevada from Fresno County north.

**Comments**  A large tree, next in size to the Sequoias in California. It is first in the United States in total stand, lumber production and veneer for plywood. Used principally in construction, for timbers, lumber, pilings, fuel, railroad ties, fencing, etc.

# Quercus agrifolia

**Common Name**  Coast Live Oak

**Family**  Fagaceae

**Leaves**  Evergreen. Alternate. Finely to coarsely-tipped. Leathery, oval to broadly elliptic. Nearly round sometimes. Dark green, glabrous above. Often convex. 1 to 3 inches long, ¾ to 2 inches wide.

**Flowers**  Male catkins occur in February to April

**Fruit**  Acorns that mature the first year. Cup is broadly top-shaped. The nut is slender, pointed. Light chestnut-brown in color. Borne singly or 2 to 4 in a cluster. 1 to 1½ inches long.

**Environment**  Full sun, partial shade. Best in the coastal area. Tolerant to heat, some cold, but not prolonged freezing.

**Pests**  Aphids, Anthracnose, Goat Moth, Mildew, Mites, Oak Root Fungus, White Fly, Scale Insects, California Oak Moth, etc.

**Propagation**  Seed, cuttings

**Rate of Growth**  Moderate to rapid

**Pruning**  Only if needed

**Seasonal Value**  Foliage, fruit

**Shape**  Massive, wide spread

**Spread**  60 to 100 feet. Diameter to 8 feet

**Height**  30 to 75 feet

**Soil**  Best in light, well-drained soil. Tolerant however. Has a deep, extensive root system.

**Use**  Specimen, shade, erosion control. Bark used for tanning.

**Origin**  Coast Ranges from Sonoma County to Baja California.

**Comments**  Should have sufficient room to grow. Wood is heavy and hard. Acorns used by Indians for food. Leaves fall after one year; fall as new leaves appear. The Spanish name was Encina (Oak). Persists in street names, suburbs, estates, etc.

# Quercus chrysolepis

**Common Name**  Maul Oak, Canyon Oak

**Family**  Fagaceae

**Leaves**  Evergreen. Thick and leathery. Elliptic to oblong or ovate. Green and glabrous above, yellowish tomentose below. Become grayish or glaucous. Entire or irregularly spiny-toothed. ¾ to 4 inches long, ½ to 1¾ inches wide.

**Flowers**  April and May

**Fruit**  Acorns. Maturing the second year.  Cup is narrow, surrounding only the base of the nut. Ovoid to oblong or ellipsoidal. 1 to 1¼ inch long.

**Environment**  Full sun. In canyons, moist slopes below 6500 feet.

**Pests**  Aphids, Scale Insects, etc.

**Propagation**  Seed, cuttings

**Rate of Growth**  Moderate

**Pruning**  As needed

**Seasonal Value**  Foliage, fruit

**Shape**  Round-headed

**Spread**  to 100 feet; diameter 2 to 3 feet

**Height**  25 to 50 or to 100 feet

**Soil**  Well-drained

**Use**  Specimen. Wood is dense and fine-grained. Seasons well and is used for tool handles, furniture, flooring.

**Origin**  In the mountains, canyons and on moist ridges and flats of the Coast Ranges, of California and southern Oregon. Also on the slopes of the Sierras, mountains of southern California, Lower California, Arizona, New Mexico.

**Comments**  Often shrub-like. Bark grayish or whitish or even black. Extremely variable.

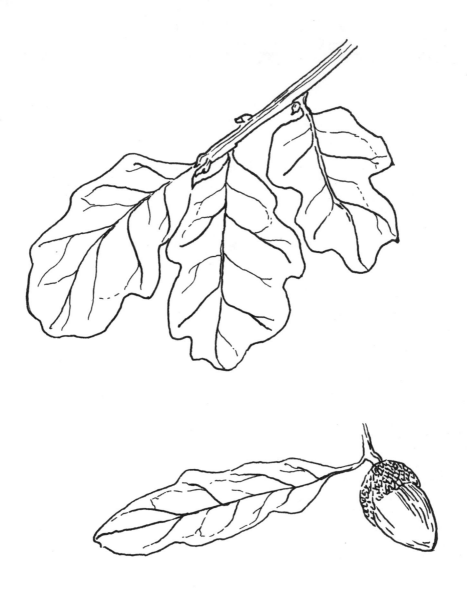

# Quercus douglasii

**Common Name**  Blue Oak

**Family**  Fagaceae

**Leaves**  Deciduous. Bluish-green. Stiff. Oblong to obovate. Shallowly and irregularly lobed or few-toothed to entire. Finely pubescent. 1½ to 4 inches long, ¾ to 2 inches wide.

**Flowers**  April and May

**Fruit**  Acorn. Variable in shape. Usually ovoid. Maturing in one season. Chestnut-brown in color. ¾ to 1¼ inches long.

**Environment**  Full sun, dry areas. In the foothills and slopes to 1500 feet, and in the north to 3000 feet.

**Pests**  Aphids, Scale Insects, White Fly, etc.

**Propagation**  Seed, cuttings

**Rate of Growth**  Slow

**Pruning**  Only as needed

**Seasonal Value**  Foliage, fruit

**Shape**  Low-branching, wide-spread

**Spread**  25 to 50 feet. Diameter 1 to 4 feet.

**Height**  to 50 feet or to 75 feet

**Soil**  Dry, well-drained

**Use**  Specimen. Wood is heavy, hard, strong, fine-grained. Used for fuel, fence posts. Squirrels eat the acorns.

**Origin**  On slopes bordering interior valleys from northern Los Angeles County to upper part of Sacramento Valley.

**Comments**  Bark is smooth, whitish

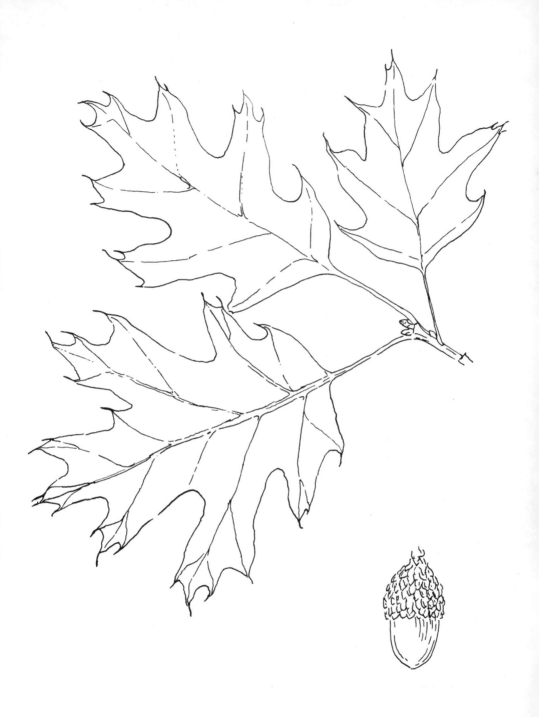

# *Quercus kelloggii*

**Common Name**  California Black Oak

**Family**  Fagaceae

**Leaves**  Deciduous. Deeply 5 to 7-lobed. Lobes ending in bristly points. New foliage is soft pink in color, bright glossy green when mature, turning yellow or orange-yellow in the fall. Grayish on both surfaces when young, before maturing. 4 to 8 inches long. 2½ to 4 inches wide.

**Flowers**  Male are in catkins, female are solitary or several on a stem. April and May.

**Fruit**  Acorns. Maturing the first year. Pale chestnut-brown. The cap is hemispherical. Encloses one-third to one-half of the nut. The nut is from one to one and one-eighth inches long.

**Environment**  Tolerant to heat and some cold. Does not do well under seacoast conditions. From 1500 to 5000 feet in north and from 4500 to 7000 feet in southern California. Full sun.

**Pests**  Aphids, scale insects

**Propagation**  Seed, cuttings

**Rate of Growth**  Slow to moderate

**Pruning**  None usually required

**Seasonal Value**  Foliage, fruit, fall color

**Shape**  Rounded

**Spread**  25 to 30 feet; 1 to 4½ feet diameter

**Height**  30 to 80 feet

**Soil**  Grows in dry, gravelly soils

**Use**  Specimen, used for fuel mostly. Wood is heavy, brittle, fine-grained.

**Origin**  California, Oregon. Most extensive range of any California Oak. From southern California (San Diego County) to southwest Oregon. In the Coast ranges and Sierra Nevada Mountains.

**Comments**  Associated with Douglas Fir, Madrone, Tanbark Oak, Ponderosa Pine. Bark is thick, nearly black, deeply furrowed.

# Quercus lobata

**Common Name**  Valley Oak, California White Oak

**Family**  Fagaceae

**Leaves**  Deciduous. Oblong to obovate. Deeply 7 to 11-lobed. Lobes often broader near apex. Green and pubescent or nearly glabrous above. Paler and pubescent, with yellow veins below. Petioles ¼ to ½ inches long. Leaves 2½ to 4 inches long, 1½ to 3 inches across.

**Flowers**  Male flowers are catkins. March and April.

**Fruit**  Acorns which mature the first year. Reddish-brown at maturity. 1¼ to 2 inches long.

**Environment**  Full sun. Tolerant to high temperatures. 2000 feet in north, 4000 feet in the south.

**Pests**  Aphids, California Oak Moth, Scales, White Fly, Mildew

**Propagation**  Seed, cuttings

**Rate of Growth**  Rapid

**Pruning**  Thin as needed

**Seasonal Value**  Foliage, fruit

**Shape**  Massive, wide-spread

**Spread**  70 feet or more. To 9 feet in diameter

**Height**  70 feet or more

**Soil**  Best in deep soils. Tolerant to some alkalinity

**Use**  Specimen, shade. Wood is hard, brittle. Used for fuel and some rough construction.

**Origin**  In Sacramento and San Joaquin Valleys south to the San Fernando Valley.

**Comments**  California's largest Oak tree. Bark is thick, light gray. May drop limbs without warning, especially where dry.

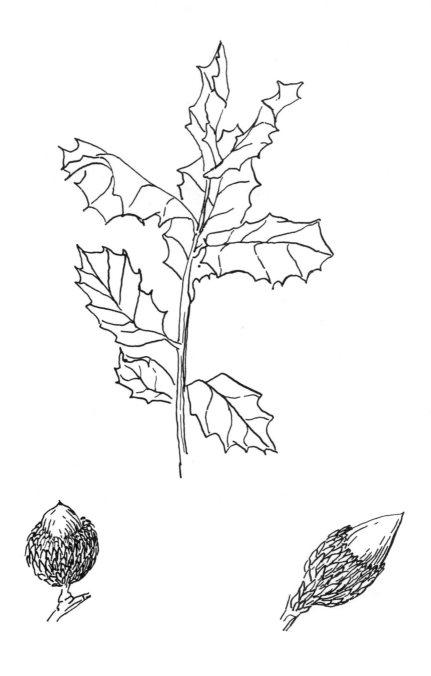

# Quercus wislizenii

**Common Name**   Interior Live Oak

**Family**   Fagaceae

**Leaves**   Evergreen. Oblong, ovate or lanceolate. Glabrous. Glossy green. With spiny margins, or entire. Usually flat. Leathery. Apex acute or rounded. 1 to 4 inches long, ¾ to 1¾ inches wide.

**Flowers**   Male catkins 1 to 1½ inches long.

**Fruit**   Acorn. Long and slender. Chestnut-brown. Two years to mature. 1 to 1½ inches long.

**Environment**   Found in valley floors, on rocky slopes, ridges. At elevations of from 2000 to 5000 feet. Full sun.

**Pests**   Aphids, Mites, Scales

**Propagation**   Seed, cuttings

**Rate of Growth**   Slow

**Pruning**   Thin as needed

**Seasonal Value**   Foliage, fruit

**Shape**   Rounded, spreading

**Spread**   Wide - often over 75 feet

**Height**   30 to 75 feet

**Soil**   Tolerant to poor, dry soil

**Use**   Specimen for large areas such as parks

**Origin**   In the Sierra foothills and on the east side of the Central Valley. From Ventura to Shasta and Siskiyou Counties.

**Comments**   The bark is thick, smooth, nearly black. Associated with Blue Oak and Digger Pine.

# Rhamnus californica

**Common Name**  California Coffeeberry

**Family**  Rhamnaceae

**Leaves**  Evergreen. Narrowly or broadly oblong. Serrulate. Usually acute. Glabrous or slightly puberulent. Alternate. Considerable variation between different plants. 1 to 3 inches long. Sometimes revolute. ½ to 1 inch wide.

**Flowers**  Greenish. In clusters (umbels). April to June.

**Fruit**  Green when young, then red, then finally black. Globose to ovoid. Apparently resembles the coffee bean, though it is not used for a beverage. July and August.

**Environment**  Full sun or partial shade. Commonly found in open woodland or on brushy slopes. Tolerant to wind. To 4000 feet.

**Pests**  Aphids, Leaf Miner.

**Propagation**  Seed, cuttings. Fresh seed September - October.

**Rate of Growth**  Rapid

**Pruning**  Tolerant, if needed.

**Seasonal Value**  Foliage, flowers, fruit

**Shape**  Tall shrub or small tree.

**Spread**  4 to 8 feet

**Height**  4 to 18 feet

**Soil**  Tolerant. Drought-tolerant. Grows naturally in rocky soil or heavy soils.

**Use**  Mass effect on slopes. Screen. Background. Container.

**Origin**  In the Coast Ranges from San Luis Obispo to Mendocino Counties. Oregon, Arizona, New Mexico.

**Comments**  Variable foliage. Bark has qualities of Cascara. Is used commercially. Branch color varies from gray to brown to reddish. Leaves may be entire.

# *Rhamnus crocea*

**Common Name**  Redberry, Buckthorn

**Family**  Rhamnaceae

**Leaves**  Evergreen. Often fascicled. Thick. Leathery. Yellowish-brown below. Margins entire to finely serrate. Elliptic to ovate or obovate. ½ to 1 inch long. About as wide.

**Flowers**  Yellowish-green. In small clusters in the leaf axils. Dioecious. Individual flowers ¼ inch across. February to May.

**Fruit**  Clear red berry. ¼ inch across. June to September.

**Environment**  Full sun or partial shade. Dry washes and canyons. Below 3000 feet.

**Pests**  Aphids

**Propagation**  Seed, cuttings. Seeds germinate readily when fresh.

**Rate of Growth**  Moderate to rapid

**Pruning**  Tolerant, if needed.

**Seasonal Value**  Foliage, flowers, fruit

**Shape**  Compact, low

**Spread**  5 to 8 feet

**Height**  5 feet

**Soil**  Tolerant. Drought-tolerant. Needs good drainage.

**Use**  On slopes, in containers. Groupings. A very adaptable plant.

**Origin**  Coast Ranges from Lake County south to Baja California.

**Comments**  Has short spiny branches. Bark on older branches is grayish. On young branches it is reddish or reddish-purple. Introduced into cultivation about 1846.

# Rhododendron macrophyllum

**Common Name**  Rhododendron, California Rose Bay

**Family**  Ericaceae

**Leaves**  Dark green, alternate, leathery.  Oblong to elliptic.  2½ to 5½ inches long.  Glabrous.  Entire.  1¼ to 2 inches wide.

**Flowers**  Rose pink to Rose-purple, rarely white.  10 stamens.  April to July.

**Fruit**  Capsule

**Environment**  Partial shade best.  In shaded woods below 4000 feet.

**Pests**  Aphids, Brachyrhinus weevil, Petal Blight.

**Propagation**  Seed, cuttings

**Rate of Growth**  Moderate

**Pruning**  After flowering.  Remove flowers.

**Seasonal Value**  Foliage, flowers

**Shape**  Upright, open

**Spread**  4 to 10 feet or more

**Height**  4 to 10 feet or more

**Soil**  Moist, organic, well-drained

**Use**  Specimen

**Origin**  Coast Ranges from Monterey County to Del Norte and Siskiyou Counties, to British Columbia.

**Comments**  Possibly toxic to sheep.  *R. occidentale* (Western azalea) has 5 stamens.

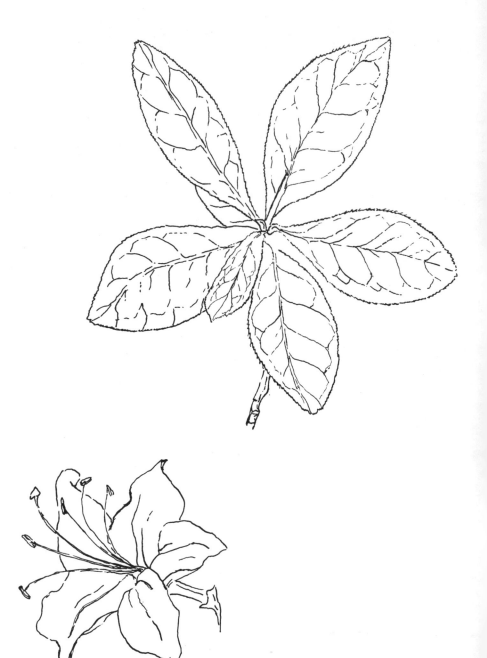

# Rhododendron occidentale

**Common Name**  Western Azalea

**Family**  Ericaceae

**Leaves**  Deciduous. Thin. Elliptic to obovate. Sparsely hairy both sides or nearly glabrous. Ciliate. Entire. Alternate. 1 to 4 inches long, ½ to 1 inch wide.

**Flowers**  White to pinkish-white, with a yellow blotch. Fragrant. Funnel-shaped. May to July.

**Fruit**  Capsule. Oblong. Pubescent. Three-eighths to three-quarters of an inch long.

**Environment**  Partial shade. Naturally along stream banks and other moist places. Below 7500 feet.

**Pests**  Brachyrhinus Weevil, Petal Blight

**Propagation**  Seed, cuttings, layering

**Rate of Growth**  Rapid

**Pruning**  Remove dead flowers. Head slightly to make more compact.

**Seasonal Value**  Foliage, flowers, fragrance

**Shape**  Erect, loosely branched

**Spread**  6 to 10 feet

**Height**  6 to 10 feet

**Soil**  Acid, moist, with sufficient organic matter

**Use**  Specimen. Shaded areas

**Origin**  California and Oregon. Coast Ranges from Santa Cruz Mountains to Shasta County and in the Sierras from southern California on northward.

**Comments**  Foliage is said to be toxic to sheep and cattle.

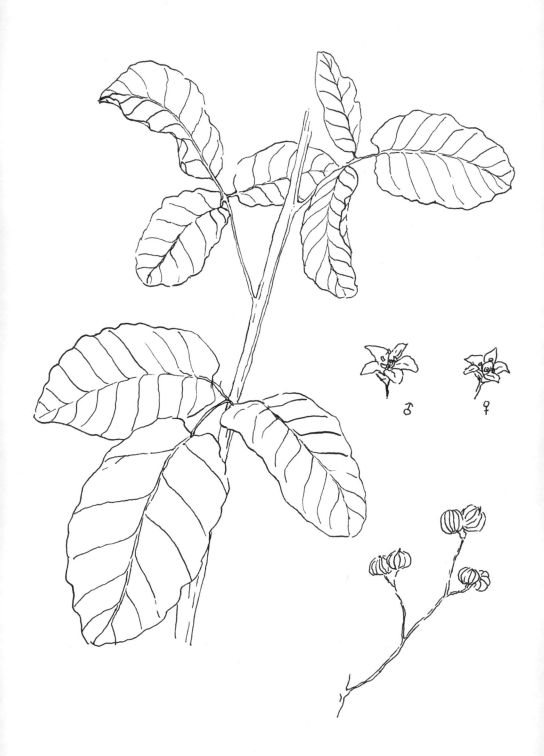

# Rhus diversiloba

**Common Name**  Poison Oak

**Family**  Anacardiaceae

**Leaves**  Deciduous. Palmately compound, with three leaflets. Orbicular to ovate, but variable. Leaflets lobed or toothed. Glabrous. 1 to 4 inches long. ½ to ¾ inches wide. Alternate.

**Flowers**  Greenish. In axillary panicles. One-eighth inch across. Early spring.

**Fruit**  White drupe. About one-eighth inch across.

**Environment**  Foothills, valleys, stream beds, mountain slopes and many other areas. From sea level to 5000 feet. Full sun, part shade.

**Pests**  Apparently clean

**Propagation**  Seed, roots, rhizomes

**Rate of Growth**  Rapid

**Pruning**  As needed

**Seasonal Value**  Foliage, fall color

**Shape**  Variable. Either erect or a vine.

**Spread**  Wide

**Height**  4 to 8 feet or more with support

**Soil**  Tolerant

**Use**  Natural areas

**Origin**  California, Oregon, Washington

**Comments**  Highly toxic skin irritant. More widespread in California than any other native plant. Was used by the Indians for various purposes. The slender, supple stems were used in making baskets. Leaves were mixed into acorn meal for baking bread. The juice from the roots and stems was used as a wart cure. A dye was used for coloring of baskets.

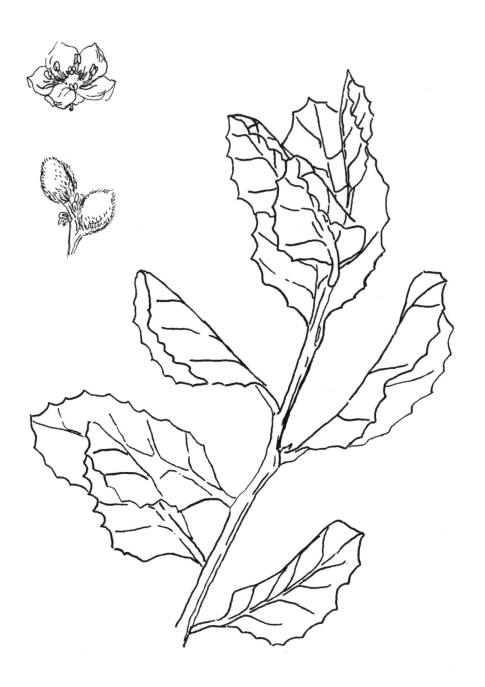

# Rhus integrifolia

**Common Name**  Lemonade Berry

**Family**  Anacardiaceae

**Leaves**  Evergreen. Alternate. Elliptic to orbicular. Thick and leathery. Dull green above. Undulated. Entire or irregularly toothed. 1 to 2½ inches long, ¾ to 1½ inches wide. May be ovate.

**Flowers**  White or pinkish. In dense terminal clusters. Individual flowers about ¼ inch across. Mostly from February to March, but sometimes from January to July.

**Fruit**  Reddish at maturity. Hairy and sticky. Can be used for flavoring beverages. Rounded, somewhat flattened. July to September.

**Environment**  Full sun or partial shade. Best near the coast. Tolerant to seacoast conditions, wind. Below 2500 feet.

**Pests**  Apparently clean

**Propagation**  Seed, cuttings. Soak in boiling water.

**Rate of Growth**  Moderate to rapid

**Pruning**  Thin if necessary

**Seasonal Value**  Foliage, flowers, fruit

**Shape**  Large shrub or small tree

**Spread**  3 to 10 feet

**Height**  3 to 10 feet or to 25 feet (rarely)

**Soil**  Tolerant. Best if irrigated about once a month during summer.

**Use**  Formal hedge, specimen, screen, background, ground cover

**Origin**  On the bluffs and mesas on the coast of southern California from Santa Barbara County to Baja California.

**Comments**  Foliage appears to be dusty. Will grow taller away from the wind. Indians and early settlers used berries for beverages, taking advantage of the sugary coating.

# Rhus laurina

**Common Name**  Laurel Sumac

**Family**  Anacardiaccae

**Leaves**  Evergreen. Ovate to lanceolate. Mucronate. Aromatic. Boat-shaped. Veins reddish. 1½ to 5 inches long to 2 inches wide. Alternate. Entire.

**Flowers**  White. Dense panicle. February and March.

**Fruit**  Whitish drupe. Glabrous. Very small, one-eighth of an inch across.

**Environment**  Ocean bluffs and canyons, dry slopes below 3000 feet. Full sun.

**Pests**  Aphids, Greedy Scale

**Propagation**  Seed, cuttings. Soak seed in hot water.

**Rate of Growth**  Moderate

**Pruning**  As needed

**Seasonal Value**  Foliage, flowers

**Shape**  Rounded. Large shrub or small tree.

**Spread**  5 to 7 feet

**Height**  5 to 7 to 13 feet

**Soil**  Tolerant. Dry.

**Use**  Specimen

**Origin**  Along the coast, from Santa Barbara County south to lower California to Riverside County.

**Comments**  Good honey bee plant.

# Rhus ovata

**Common Name**  Sugar Bush, Sugar Sumac

**Family**  Anacardiaceae

**Leaves**  Evergreen. Alternate. Glossy. Entire or with a few small sharp teeth. Pinkish-green. Usually boat-shaped. Ovate. Thick and leathery. Reddish at maturity. ¾ to 1½ inches wide, 1 to 4 inches long.

**Flowers**  Whitish or pinkish. In dense terminal clusters. Pink buds. Individual flowers three-sixteenths of an inch long. March to May.

**Fruit**  Reddish drupe. Coated with a sugary secretion. In tight clusters. Flattened. ¼ inch in diameter. June to October.

**Environment**  Full sun. Tolerant to seacoast if not exposed directly to salt spray and direct sea winds. Dry slopes below 2500 feet.

**Pests**  Aphids

**Propagation**  Seed, cuttings. Remove pulp, soak in boiling water.

**Rate of Growth**  Moderate to rapid

**Pruning**  Thin as needed. Not severe.

**Seasonal Value**  Foliage, flowers, fruit

**Shape**  Roundish, erect or spreading

**Spread**  2½ to 10 feet

**Height**  2½ to 10 feet

**Soil**  Tolerant to summer water if well-drained. Taproot.

**Use**  Specimen. Background. Screen. Hedge. Espalier.

**Origin**  The dry hills in southern California from Santa Barbara to San Diego Counties. Santa Cruz and Santa Catalina Islands.

**Comments**  Indians used the fruit for a sugary drink.

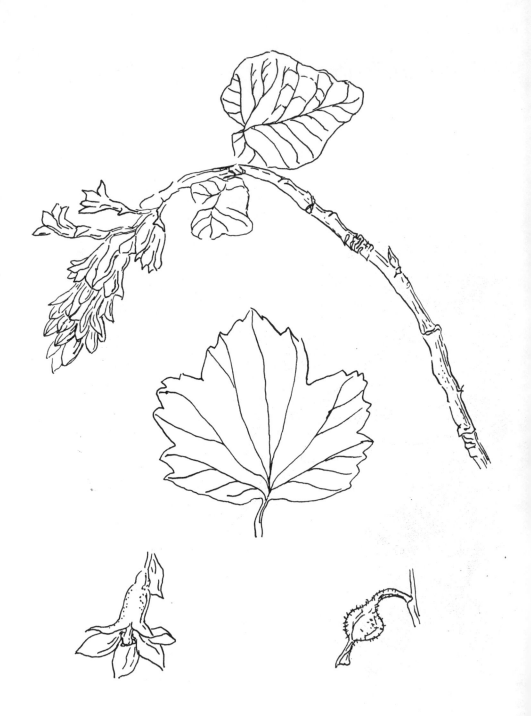

# Ribes sanguineum var. glutinosum

**Common Name**  Pink Flowering Currant, Red-Flowering Currant

**Family**  Saxifragaceae

**Leaves**  Deciduous to semi-deciduous. Orbicular to cordate. 3 to 5 lobed. Viscid (glutinous). Finely serrate to crenate. Green both sides. Aromatic. Mostly glabrous above. Pubescent below, especially on veins. Terminal lobe usually broader than long.

**Flowers**  Pale to deep pink. 15 to 40 in pendulous racemes. Individual flowers funnel-shaped. February to March.

**Fruit**  Bluish-black or black berry. Usually glaucous. ¼ to three-eighths of an inch across. Edible.

**Environment**  Partial shade. Below 2000 feet. Chaparral areas. On moist slopes.

**Pests**  Aphids, Scale Insects, Currant Bud Mite

**Propagation**  Seed, cuttings, division.  Stratify seed 3 months.

**Rate of Growth**  Rapid

**Pruning**  As needed to control

**Seasonal Value**  Foliage, flowers, fruit

**Shape**  Upright, spreading

**Spread**  5 to 12 feet

**Height**  5 to 12 feet

**Soil**  Best if moist, but tolerant

**Use**  Specimen. Background. Group plantings. Bank cover.

**Origin**  Coast Ranges from Del Norte and Humboldt to Santa Barbara and San Luis Obispo Counties.

**Comments**  Old bark is brownish. The leaves of *Ribes sanguineum* are whitish-hairy below and the racemes are more erect.

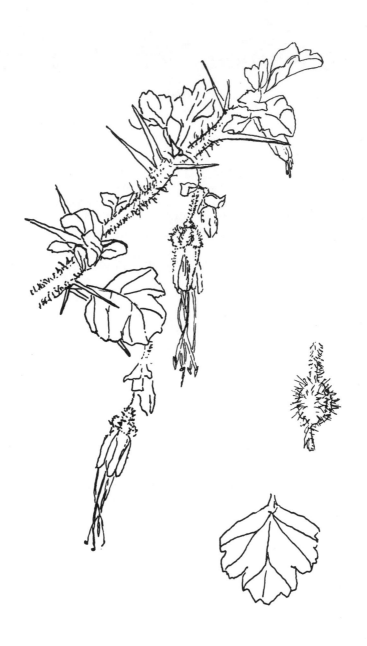

# Ribes speciosum

**Common Name**  Fuchsia-flowered Gooseberry

**Family**  Saxifragaceae

**Leaves**  Nearly evergreen. Alternate. Thick and leathery. Orbicular, oblong to obovate. Cuneate base. 3 to 5 veined from the base. Slightly 3 to 5-lobed or toothed at the apex. Entire along lower half. Glabrous or slightly hairy above. Dark green. ¾ to 1½ inches across.

**Flowers**  Deep crimson. One or two drooping peduncles in clusters. With long protruding stamens. January to May.

**Fruit**  Ovoid berry. Densely glandular-bristly. Three-eighths to one-half of an inch long.

**Environment**  Best in partial shade, with sufficient moisture. Will grow in full sun with sufficient water. Sea level to 2000 feet.

**Pests**  Aphids

**Propagation**  Seed, cuttings

**Rate of Growth**  Moderate to rapid

**Pruning**  If needed

**Seasonal Value**  Foliage, flowers, fruit

**Shape**  Tall, upright, stiff

**Spread**  3 to 6 feet

**Height**  3 to 10 feet

**Soil**  Moist, well-drained

**Use**  Specimen. Background. Barrier. Effective under Pines, with Ceanothus.

**Origin**  California. From Santa Clara and Monterey Counties south to San Diego County, along the coast.

**Comments**  Has three conspicuous spines at the nodes. Internodes are bristly. In cultivation since 1828.

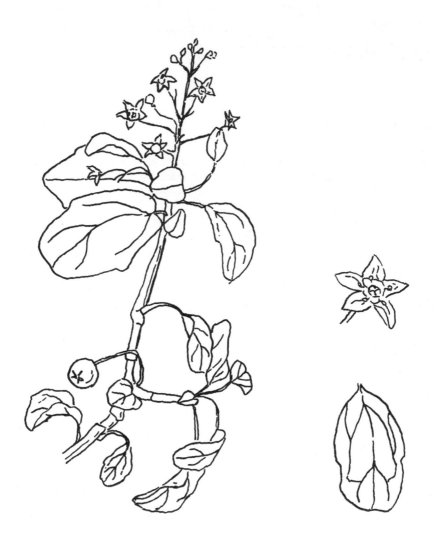

# Ribes viburnifolium

**Common Name**  Evergreen Currant

**Family**  Saxifragaceae

**Leaves**  Evergreen. Dark green, glabrous. Resinous-dotted below. Thick. Ovate, obovate to orbicular. Entire or few-toothed, or lobed. Alternate. Aromatic. ¾ to 1½ inches.

**Flowers**  Rose to light pink. Small. Few to several in erect clusters (racemes). January to April. ¼ inch across.

**Fruit**  Red. Round. ¼ inch in diameter. May.

**Environment**  Probably best in partial shade. More vigorous in full sun, with more flowers, but if too hot, leaves may scorch.

**Pests**  Aphids

**Propagation**  Seed, cuttings, layering. Self-layering.

**Rate of Growth**  Rapid

**Pruning**  Will tolerate moderate pruning, but prune only as needed.

**Seasonal Value**  Foliage, flowers, fruit.

**Shape**  Upright, spreading, trailing.

**Spread**  12 feet

**Height**  3 to 6 feet

**Soil**  Moist. Drought-tolerant when established. Best with some water.

**Use**  Ground cover. Bank cover. Around large rocks. Effective trailing over retaining walls.

**Origin**  Santa Catalina Island and lower California.

**Comments**  Stems are wine-red in color. Has no thorns so does not resemble other species of Ribes. The one vein from the base is characteristic. The foliage is darker in the shade.

# Romneya coulteri

**Common Name**  Matilija Poppy, Coulter Poppy

**Family**  Papaveraceae

**Leaves**  Semi-deciduous. Grayish-green. Alternate. Simple. Pinnatified. Sparingly dentate. Slightly ciliate sometimes. 2 to 4 inches long. Leaf lobes lanceolate. Terminal one three-cleft. 3 to 5 lobed.

**Flowers**  White, with golden centers. Soft, with the appearance of crepe paper. Stamens conspicuous. To 9 inches across. May to August.

**Fruit**  Ovoid capsule. Covered with dense, spreading hairs. Fruit is 1 to 2 inches long. Tapering at both ends. Seeds numerous and black.

**Environment**  Full sun. Naturally from 1000 to 2000 feet.

**Pests**  Aphids

**Propagation**  Seed, cuttings, suckers, division. (Root cuttings best.)

**Rate of Growth**  Slow to start from seed. Rapid when established.

**Pruning**  Remove dead parts, cut back in fall to the soil-level.

**Seasonal Value**  Foliage, flowers

**Shape**  Upright, round

**Spread**  Wide

**Height**  3 to 8 feet

**Soil**  Tolerant, but best where has good drainage. Deep water during flowering period. Invasive.

**Use**  On hot, sunny slopes, along roads. Erosion control. Ground cover. Good for cut flowers.

**Origin**  California coastal mountains. Santa Barbara County south to San Diego County. In Mexico.

**Comments**  Has a few spines on the petioles and margins.

# Rubus parviflorus

**Common Name**  Thimble Berry

**Family**  Rubiaceae

**Leaves**  Deciduous. Alternate. Serrate. Palmately 3 to 5-lobed. Cordate at the base. Orbicular. Glabrous to sparsely hairy above. Pubescent below. To 6 inches across and very soft to the touch.

**Flowers**  White to pink. 4 to 7 in a terminal cluster. 1 to 2 inches across. March to August.

**Fruit**  Red. ½ to ¾ inches across. Like a thimble in shape. Edible.

**Environment**  Partial shade. From sea level to 9000 feet. Open woods and in canyons.

**Pests**  Aphids

**Propagation**  Seed, cuttings

**Rate of Growth**  Moderate

**Pruning**  As desired

**Seasonal Value**  Foliage, flowers, fruit

**Shape**  Upright, branching

**Spread**  3 to 5 feet

**Height**  4 to 6 feet

**Soil**  Moist, well-drained

**Use**  Specimen. For shaded areas.

**Origin**  From the San Diego mountains north through the Sierra Nevadas to Siskiyou and Humboldt Counties to Alaska, and also in other parts of the western United States to Michigan.

**Comments**  Has a soft textured foliage.

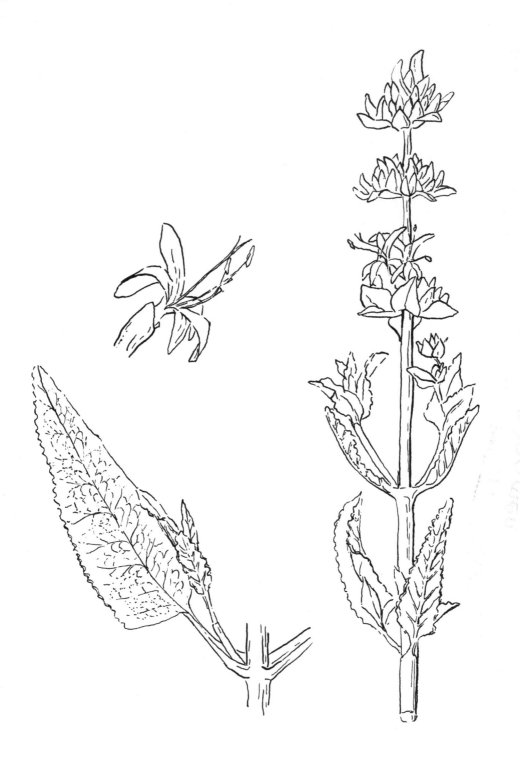

# Salvia leucophylla

**Common Name** Purple Sage

**Family** Labiatae

**Leaves** Evergreen or semi-evergreen. Opposite. Crenate. Aromatic. Grayish-green above, white hairy below. Oblong to lanceolate. Young leaves reddish or purplish-green. 2 to 3 inches long. ½ inch wide.

**Flowers** Pink to purplish. Spaced along the stem in 3 to 5 whorled clusters. Individual flowers to ¾ inch long. May to June. Irregular. Monoecious. Nearly sessile.

**Fruit** Brownish-gray nutlet

**Environment** Full sun. Tolerant to heat. On dry, barren slopes below 2000 feet.

**Pests** Aphids

**Propagation** Seed, cuttings, division

**Rate of Growth** Rapid

**Pruning** Remove old flowers if desired

**Seasonal Value** Foliage, flowers, fragrance

**Shape** Compact, spreading

**Spread** 5 feet or more

**Height** 5 feet or more

**Soil** Tolerant, but best in gravelly, well-drained soil. On the dry side.

**Use** On dry slopes. Effective with Matilija Poppy.

**Origin** From San Luis Obsipo south to Orange County. Along the coast.

**Comments** May drop foliage if too dry. May hybridize with *Salvia clevelandii.*

# Sambucus caerulea

**Common Name**  Blue Elderberry

**Family**  Caprifoliaceae

**Leaves**  Deciduous. Opposite. Odd-pinnately compound. With 5,7 or 9 leaflets. Leaves to 12 inches long. Leaflets 1 to 4 inches long. Ovate or oblong to lanceolate. Glabrous. Serrate except near apex. Oblique at base. Sometimes hairy.

**Flowers**  White to creamy-white. In flat-topped clusters. 2 to 6 inches across. Fragrant. In cymes. April to August.

**Fruit**  In clusters. Blue, with a bloom. A drupe, with 3 to 5 seeds. ¼ inch across. Used for jams, jellies, pies, wine. July to September.

**Environment**  Full sun or partial shade. Open areas up to 10,000 feet.

**Pests**  Aphids

**Propagation**  Seed, cuttings. Stratify seed 3 months.

**Rate of Growth**  Moderate to rapid

**Pruning**  A rampant grower, so thin out as needed

**Seasonal Value**  Foliage, flowers, fruit

**Shape**  Small tree or large shrub. Variable shape

**Spread**  15 to 30 feet

**Height**  15 to 30 feet

**Soil**  Best if in light, well-drained, moist soil

**Use**  Specimen, screen, wind-break

**Origin**  From San Diego County north through the Sierras and Coast Ranges to British Columbia. Also to Idaho.

**Comments**  Fruit is edible, but the bark is toxic. *Sambucus racemosa* is Red Elderberry. *Sambucus callicarpa racemosa* is said to have poisonous fruit.

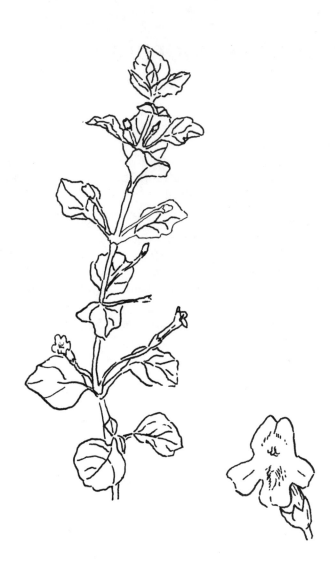

# Satureja douglasii

**Common Name**  Yerba Buena

**Family**  Labiatae

**Leaves**  Evergreen. Opposite. Roundish. To one inch in length. With a strong mint odor. Entire plant sparsely hairy. Crenate. ½ to 3 inches long. Ovate. Glabrous. Ciliate. Sometimes entire.

**Flowers**  Small, white, or lavender-tinted. Singly in the axils. April to September.

**Fruit**  Nutlets. Brown. Glossy.

**Environment**  Full sun along the coast. Partial shade inland. Probably best in partial shade. Below 3000 feet. In Coast Ranges.

**Pests**  Aphids

**Propagation**  Seed, stolons, cuttings

**Rate of Growth**  Rapid

**Pruning**  Cut down as needed. May become leggy.

**Seasonal Value**  Foliage, flowers, fragrance

**Shape**  Low, flat

**Spread**  To 3 feet or more

**Height**  Prostrate to 6 inches

**Soil**  Rich and moist is best.

**Use**  Ground cover. Dried leaves for a tea.

**Origin**  From Los Angeles County to British Columbia. Santa Catalina Island.

**Comments**  A creeping perennial. San Francisco was originally named for this plant.

# Sequoia sempervirens

**Common Name**  Coast Redwood

**Family**  Taxodiaceae

**Leaves**  Evergreen. With two types - juvenile and adult. Juvenile somewhat similar to those of the Giant Sequoia, while the mature foliage is in flat sprays. Juvenile ½ inch long, awl-shaped. Adult ½ to ¾ inches long. Linear, with 2 gray bands below.

**Flowers**  Monoecious. In catkins. Male with numerous stamens, greenish. Female also greenish and with numerous scales.

**Fruit**  An ovoid cone. ½ to 1½ inches long. About one inch across. In clusters. Seeds narrowly winged. Germination rate of seed usually about 25%. Reddish-brown.

**Environment**  Best in a humid environment. Tolerant to cold and some heat. Full sun. Tolerates seacoast, but protect from direct wind. Grows naturally from sea-level to 2500 feet. Best from 50 to 100 degrees.

**Pests**  Cypress Scale, Bark Beetles, Flat-headed Twig Borer, Mites, Bark Canker, Needle Blight, Botrytis.

**Propagation**  Seed, cuttings

**Rate of Growth**  Rapid

**Pruning**  Remove the suckers. Best to cut into bark in doing this.

**Seasonal Value**  Foliage, cones, bark.

**Shape**  Pyramidal, with branches spreading horizontally

**Spread**  20 to 40 feet

**Height**  100 to 340 feet

**Soil**  Best in deep, rich, well-drained, moist soil. Is comparatively shallow-rooted.

**Use**  Specimen, background, hedge, in groves. For lumber, burls.

**Origin**  From Southwestern Oregon south to San Luis Obispo County. Extends 30 miles inland.

**Comments**  Over 30 varieties have been found in fossil form. It was once distributed over 4 continents. Is the world's tallest tree. Is the official tree of California, since 1937 - through the combined efforts of the Santa Barbara Botanic Garden, State Senator James Hollister and the Native Sons of the Golden West. Bark is fire-resistant. Will stump-sprout. Normal life-expectancy is from 1000 to 1500 years. The oldest was 2200 years. The bark is from 3 to 12 inches thick. Cultivar 'Aptos Blue'.

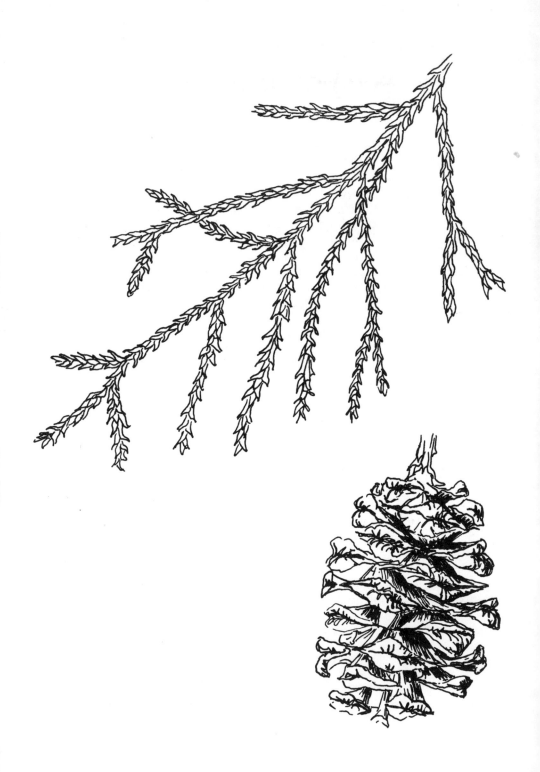

# Sequoiadendron giganteum

**Common Name**  Giant Sequoia

**Family**  Taxodiaceae

**Leaves**  Evergreen. Overlapping. Awl-shaped. Close to the branches. Bluish-green when young. Bright green when mature. Persisting for 3 to 4 years. To ½ inch long.

**Flowers**  Monoecious. Catkins. Male terminal in leaf axils, female on twigs.

**Fruit**  Dark reddish-brown, ovoid cones. 2 to 3 inches long. 1 to 1½ inches across. Maturing the second year.

**Environment**  Full sun. Tolerant to cold, even at high altitudes. Grows in a humid environment. From 4000 to 8000 feet. West slope of the Sierras.

**Pests**  Aphids, Mites, Cedar tree borer, Needle Blight, Sequoia Pitch Moth, Mealy bug, Scale insects. Botrytis.

**Propagation**  Seed, cuttings. Stratify 2½ months.

**Rate of Growth**  Moderate to rapid

**Pruning**  None should be necessary

**Seasonal Value**  Foliage, Cones

**Shape**  Pyramidal

**Spread**  75 to 100 feet; 10 to 35 feet in diameter

**Height**  150 to 300 feet; tallest living is 281 feet

**Soil**  Prefers a deep, rich, well-drained soil, with sufficient moisture. With a deep root system.

**Use**  Specimen, Large hedge.

**Origin**  From Placer to Tulare County at the above elevations.

**Comments**  The largest tree in the world in volume. Has heavy thick branches which grow upwards at first and then curve downward. From 1000 to 3000 years of age. Bark is 1 to 2 inches thick, deeply furrowed, spongy, reddish-brown, and to 24 inches in thickness. Does not do too well in the Bay Area. Is fire-resistant. Grows in 26 isolated groves.

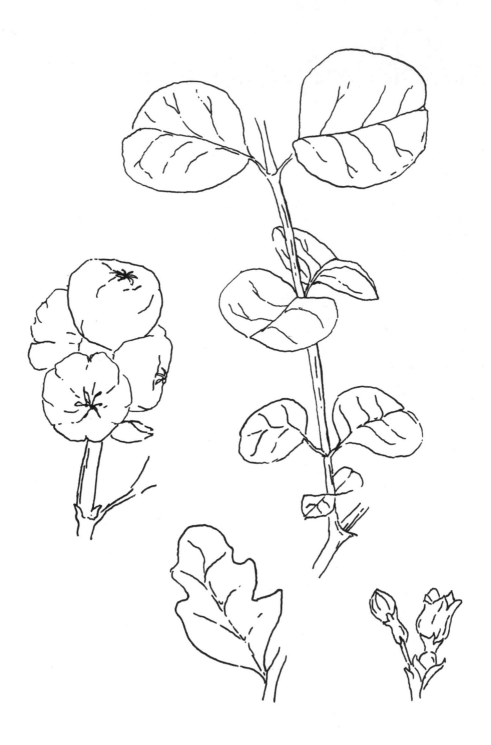

# Symphoricarpos albus

**Common Name**  Snowberry

**Family**  Caprifoliaceae

**Leaves**  Deciduous. Opposite. Entire or lobed. Oval to elliptic to orbicular. Dark green and glabrous above. Pubescent below. ¾ to 2 inches long, ½ to 1½ inches wide.

**Flowers**  White to pinkish. Each to ¼ inch long. In short peduncled racemes. May to July.

**Fruit**  Nutlets. White. Nearly tasteless. Spongy. ½ inch in length. July to November.

**Environment**  In shaded areas, in canyons and streams below 4000 feet. In the California foothills and Coast Ranges.

**Pests**  Aphids, Mildew

**Propagation**  Cuttings

**Rate of Growth**  Rapid

**Pruning**  To keep from being leggy

**Seasonal Value**  Foliage, flowers, fruit

**Shape**  Erect or spreading

**Spread**  Wide

**Height**  2 to 6 feet

**Soil**  Well drained. Suckers are produced. Rhizomes make this a potential pest plant.

**Use**  As a shade plant in a wild garden or wooded area. A poisonous drug, saponin, is produced in the leaves. Was used by the Indians for colds and stomach ache. See below.

**Origin**  Coast Ranges from Monterey County to the Sierra Nevadas to Alaska. Also Montana.

**Comments**  Very common shrub in North America. The roots were pounded and used medicinally. The fruit is a strong laxative. This is a good honey plant. Produces a white honey. Is an important wild life food plant.

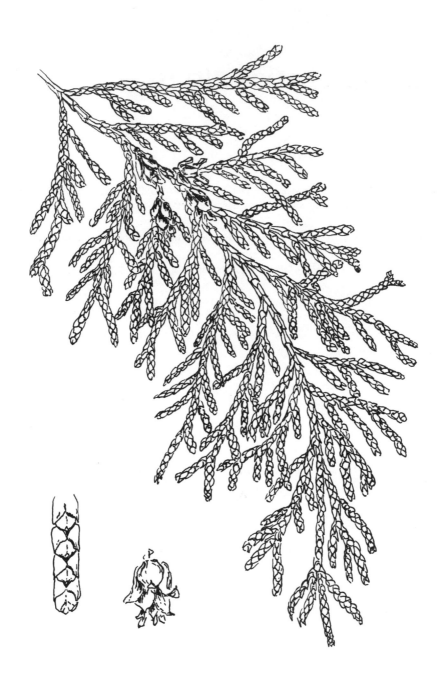

# Thuja plicata

**Common Name**  Giant Arborvitae, Western Redcedar

**Family**  Cupressaceae

**Leaves**  Evergreen. Bright green and glossy above. Usually with whitish spots below. Scale-like and arranged in sprays. Aromatic.

**Flowers**  May and early June

**Fruit**  Cones. Clustered near the ends of the branches. About three-eighths of an inch long. With 8 to 10 leathery scales. Cones cinnamon-brown. Persisting until following summer. Maturing late August. Heavy production.

**Environment**  Full sun or partial shade. Best in cool humid areas. Tolerant of extremes in heat, cold. Sea level to 7000 feet.

**Pests**  Borers and various fungi.

**Propagation**  Seed, cuttings. Stratify 2 months.

**Rate of Growth**  Slow

**Pruning**  Usually not needed

**Seasonal Value**  Foliage, cones

**Shape**  Pyramidal, formal

**Spread**  35 to 60 feet; diameter to 16 feet

**Height**  to 200 feet

**Soil**  Tolerant. Best if rich, moist, well-drained. With a shallow root system.

**Use**  Specimen. Hedge. Wood is light, brittle, weather-resistant. Used for shingles, boat hulls, home construction, totem poles, etc.

**Origin**  Coast Ranges from Mendocino County northward to Oregon, Washington, Alaska, British Columbia and also Montana.

**Comments**  Also used for baskets, fish lines, ropes, clothing (bark). Wood is buoyant. Some cultivars include: 'Aurea', 'Aurea variegata', 'Elegantissima'. Indians used as a base for totem poles. Bark is a grayish-brown. Seldom in pure stands. Very susceptible to fire injury.

# *Tsuga heterophylla*

**Common Name**  Western Hemlock, Coast Hemlock, Alaska Pine

**Family**  Pinaceae

**Leaves**  Evergreen.  Leaves attached singly.  From ¼ to 1 inch in length.  To 1/12 inch wide. Flat, grooved above.With blunt, rounded ends.  Dark to yellowish-green.  Whitish bands below.  Soft-textured. In flat sprays. Linear.

**Flowers**  Male: yellowish; female: purplish

**Fruit**  Small cones.  ¾ to 1¼ inches long.  Pendulous.  Ovoid.

**Environment**  Usually below 2000 feet.  On wooded slopes.  Full sun.

**Pests**  Comparatively few.  Hemlock Borer, Hemlock Looper, Spruce Needle Miner, Blister Rust.

**Propagation**  Seed, cuttings.  Seedlings tolerant to much shade. (Stratify 3 months.

**Rate of Growth**  Rapid

**Pruning**  Not usually necessary

**Seasonal Value**  Foliage, cones

**Shape**  Narrowly pyramidal.  Base of trunk swollen.

**Spread**  Diameter 3 to 4 feet

**Height**  125 to 160 (200) feet

**Soil**  Moist, sandy.  Needs water in the summer.  Tolerant to a wide variety, but best if deep, organic, well-drained.

**Use**  Lumber, ties, shingles, pulpwood, tan bark, wildlife food.  Background, screen, hedge.

**Origin**  Along the coast from Sonoma County north to Alaska.  Also Idaho and Montana.

**Comments**  Produces a good crop of cones every 2 to 5 years.  Not tolerant to long dry periods.  Not tolerant to winds, hot sun.  Bark valuable for tanning.  Wood more durable than of other Hemlocks.  Is the most common and the most widely distributed tree of the coniferous rain forests of the northwest coast.  Is one of the most important trees for commercial use in the world.

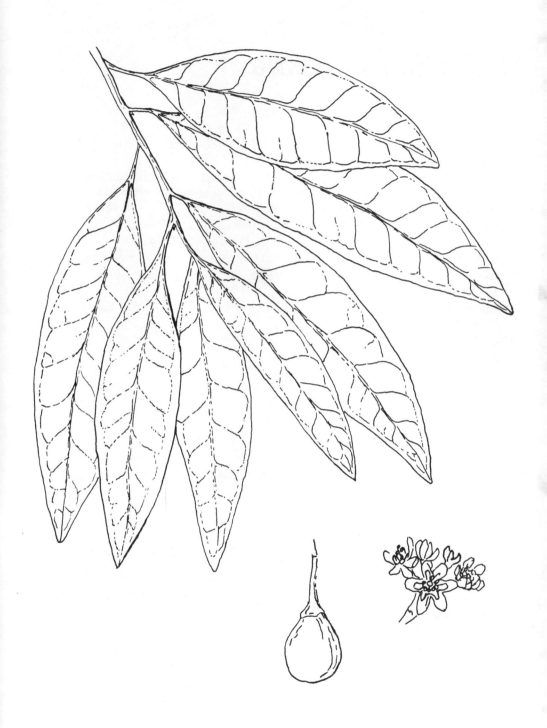

# Umbellularia californica

**Common Name** California Bay, California Laurel, Oregon Myrtle

**Family** Lauraceae

**Leaves** Evergreen. Alternate. Thick and leathery. Oblong to lanceolate. Entire. 3 to 5 inches long. ¾ to 1½ inches wide. Aromatic. Dark green. Glabrous.

**Flowers** Small, yellowish. In small dense umbels. December to May.

**Fruit** An ovoid drupe. Yellowish-green at first, then becoming purplish-brown at maturity. August to December. About one inch in length.

**Environment** Full sun or partial shade. Better in some shade in hot areas. Tolerant to heat, cold, wind. Canyons and valleys below 5000 feet.

**Pests** Aphids, Greedy Scale, Ivy Scale, Soft Brown Scale, Thrips, White Fly, Laurel White Fly, Leaf Blotch Miner, Inconspicuous White Fly.

**Propagation** Seed, cuttings (crack seed first)

**Rate of Growth** Rapid

**Pruning** Train when young to single trunk if desired. Thin as needed

**Seasonal Value** Foliage, flowers, fruit

**Shape** Ascending branches. With a rounded top.

**Spread** 30 to 50 to 100 feet

**Height** 20 to 75 to 100 feet

**Soil** Best if in fertile, moist, deep, well-drained soil. Roots are of average depth.

**Use** Specimen, hedge, container. Leaves as spice in cooking. Fruit roasted and eaten by Indians. Shade.

**Origin** Coast Ranges and Sierra Nevadas from San Diego County to northwest California and southwest Oregon.

**Comments** May be top-heavy if not thinned periodically. Much sucker growth. Wood very hard, close-grained. Used for bowls, etc. Often called Myrtle wood. In the San Francisco Bay Area has shown die-back, perhaps as the result of periodic drought. Produces much litter. Leaves were used medicinally and also as a flea repellent.

# Vaccinium ovatum

**Common Name**  California Huckleberry

**Family**  Ericaceae

**Leaves**  Evergreen. Alternate. Glossy. Ovate to oblong. Serrate. Branchlets pubescent. Leathery. Acute. Glabrous. One conspicuous vein from the base. ½ to 1¼ inches long and ¼ to ½ inch wide. New leaves bronzy.

**Flowers**  White to pink. Bell-shaped. In few-flowered axillary racemes. March to May.

**Fruit**  Black with no bloom. A berry. Ovoid. About ¼ inch long. Edible. September to December.

**Environment**  Full sun or partial shade. Will grow in the sun in the cooler areas, but does best in some shade. Naturally in dry slopes, canyons below 2500 feet.

**Pests**  Greedy Scale

**Propagation**  Seed, cuttings. Place seed in refrigerator for 3 months.

**Rate of Growth**  Slow

**Pruning**  Tolerant to severe pruning, but usually need not be pruned.

**Seasonal Value**  Foliage, flowers, fruit

**Shape**  Upright, compact

**Spread**  3 to 5 feet

**Height**  2 to 8 feet

**Soil**  Acid, well-drained. Best if has moisture. Add an acid fertilizer twice a year.

**Use**  Border, hedge, container, below large conifers, etc. Fruit for jams, jellies, pies. Cut greens used by the floral trade.

**Origin**  From San Diego County to Del Norte County to British Columbia.

**Comments**  The species *saporosum* has berries that are glaucous and are a better flavor, more pear-shaped.

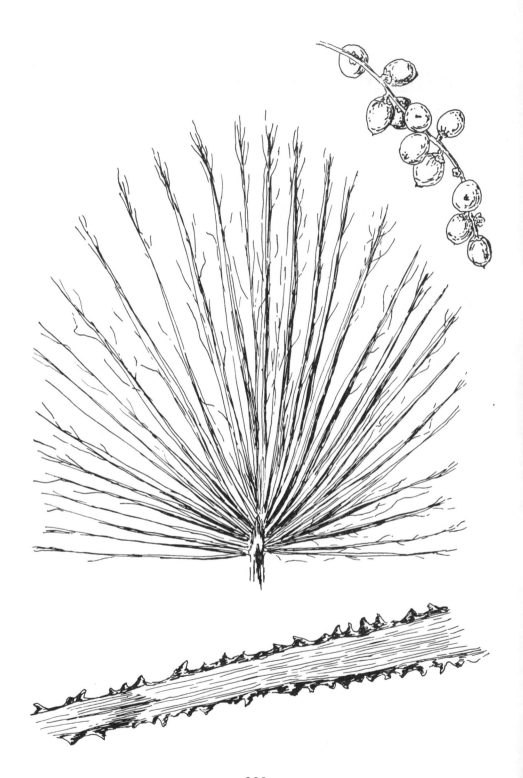

# *Washingtonia filifera*

**Common Name**  California Fan Palm

**Family**  Palmaceae

**Leaves**  Evergreen. Fan-shaped. Deeply slashed. Margins with many thread-like filaments. Grayish-green. With 40 to 70 folds. 3 to 6 feet across. Petioles to 5 feet long. With hooked spines marginal.

**Flowers**  Creamy-white. Numerous. In clusters all along the stalks. Persisting. Stalk from 8 to 10 feet long. May and June. Fragrant.

**Fruit**  Black, ovoid. In large clusters along the stalk. Thin-skinned. Sugary. Edible. June to August.

**Environment**  Full sun. Tolerant to heat and to some cold, but not to prolonged freezing. To 22 degrees. In groves in moist, alkaline areas. Below 3500 feet.

**Pests**  Crown Rot

**Propagation**  Seed

**Rate of Growth**  Moderate to rapid

**Pruning**  Remove dead foliage if desired

**Seasonal Value**  Foliage, flowers, fruit, fragrance

**Shape**  Upright, with a round top

**Spread**  8 to 20 feet, diameter to 3 feet

**Height**  20 to 80 feet

**Soil**  Best in light, moist, well-drained soil. Fibrous-rooted. Tolerant to saline, alkaline soils, some drought.

**Use**  Specimen. For parks, large areas.

**Origin**  Colorado and Mohave Deserts. Also in southwest Arizona.

**Comments**  This is the only palm native to California. Has been used to line wide streets. Young trees can be grown in containers. Indians used for food. The terminal buds and the fruit are edible. Seed was made into a meal. Leaves used as thatch for shelter. Threads used to bind baskets.

# Woodwardia fimbriata

**Common Name**  Giant Chain Fern

**Family**  Polypodiaceae

**Leaves**  Fronds to 10 feet in length. From 12 to 20 inches in width. Bi-pinnately divided. Herbaceous perennial. Coarse-textured. Sori arranged chain-like, parallel to the midrib. Segments of fronds serrulate or entire, 3 to 12 inches long.

**Flowers**  None

**Fruit**  Spores within the chain-like sori on the underside of the fronds.

**Environment**  Always in moist areas, usually in partial shade. Tolerant to 20 degrees. From 100 to 8000 feet.

**Pests**  Foliar Nematode, Mealybug, Mites

**Propagation**  Spores, Division

**Rate of Growth**  Slow to start

**Pruning**  Remove old fronds to ground

**Seasonal Value**  Fronds

**Shape**  Arching

**Spread**  9 feet or more

**Height**  To 9 feet

**Soil**  Light, moist, well-drained best. With sufficient organic matter. Spreads by woody rhizomes.

**Use**  For shaded areas, near pools, in wooded areas

**Origin**  Throughout California except seldom in the Sierras. To British Columbia and Arizona.

**Comments**  Fronds emerge from a woody crown. Largest of California ferns. Fairly tolerant to neglect, but better appearance if irrigated and pruned periodically.

# Zauschneria californica

**Common Name**  California Fuchsia, Hummingbird Fuchsia

**Family**  Onagraceae

**Leaves**  Evergreen. Alternate. Variable. Green or grayish. Linear to broadly lanceolate. Entire plant hairy. ½ to 1½ inches long, to ¼ inch wide. Ovate to oblong. Entire or toothed.

**Flowers**  In terminal spikes. Salmon-scarlet. Trumpet-shaped. 1½ to 2 inches in length. Attract hummingbirds. August to October.

**Fruit**  Capsule. Linear. Angular, with hairy seeds.

**Environment**  Full sun. To 10 degrees. Dry, gravelly areas mostly below 3500 feet. In valleys and foothills.

**Pests**  Aphids

**Propagation**  Seed, cuttings, division

**Rate of Growth**  Moderate to rapid

**Pruning**  Prune to ground in spring if necessary

**Seasonal Value**  Foliage, flowers

**Shape**  Low, rounded mat

**Spread**  18 inches or more

**Height**  18 to 36 inches

**Soil**  Light, well-drained. Needs little water once established.

**Use**  Ground cover. Rock walls. Slopes. Rock Gardens.

**Origin**  From Sonoma and Lake counties to Baja California.

**Comments**  Spreads by layering and by rhizomes. May become a pest.

# PLANTS FOR
# PARTICULAR SITUATIONS

The following lists are somewhat arbitrary. While certain plants do best or are tolerant to certain situations, various factors may affect their placement in these categories. Also, while many California natives are tolerant to full sun and/or to drought, at the same time they might present a better appearance in the landscape if they are grown in part shade and/or if given periodic irrigation.

Many California natives are not so tolerant to full sun and do not do well unless they are grown in at least some shade and unless they do receive sufficient moisture.

Plants for use as hedges and/or screens should be allowed to grow to normal size and should be given sufficient room in which to grow normally. Very few plants, native or exotic, present a good appearance when they are sheared.

Plants that are listed as tolerant to seacoast conditions may not do well if exposed to direct ocean winds and ocean spray. If given just a little protection, they might then do very well in the seacoast situation.

Also, it might be emphasized that California natives might well be grown along with exotic plants requiring the same type of environment.

Finally, when plants are grown away from the San Francisco bay area, for example at higher elevations or in the hot valley regions, they may not do well or they may have to be put into categories other than those listed below.

### Best in Full Sun

*Abies bracteata*
*Abies concolor*
*Abies magnifica*
*Adenostoma fasciculatum*
*Amelanchier alnifolia*
*Arctostaphylos densiflora*
*Arctostaphylos edmundsii*
*Arctostaphylos hookeri*
*Arctostaphylos uva-ursi*
*Artemisia pycnocephala*
*Atriplex lentiformis var. breweri*

*Lyonothamnus floribundus*
*var. asplenifolius*
*Mahonia nevinii*
*Mahonia pinnata*
*Pinus contorta*
*Pinus coulteri*
*Pinus muricata*
*Pinus ponderosa*
*Pinus radiata*
*Pinus sabiniana*
*Pinus torreyana*

*Baccharis pilularis*
*Calocedrus decurrens*
*Ceanothus gloriosus*
*Ceanothus griseus var. horizontalis*
*Ceanothus impressus*
*Ceanothus purpureus*
*Cercis occidentalis*
*Cercocarpus betuloides
   var. traskiae*
*Cercocarpus ledifolius*
*Chamaecyparis lawsoniana*
*Cupressus macrocarpa*
*Dendromecon harfordii*
*Eriogonum fasciculatum*
*Eriogonum giganteum*
*Fremontodendron californicum*
*Fremontodendron mexicanum*
*Galvezia speciosa*
*Juglans hindsii*

*Platanus racemosa*
*Prunus ilicifolia*
*Prunus lyonii*
*Pseudotsuga menziesii*
*Quercus agrifolia*
*Quercus chrysolepis*
*Quercus douglasii*
*Quercus kelloggii*
*Quercus lobata*
*Quercus wislizenii*
*Rhus laurina*
*Rhus ovata*
*Romneya coulteri*
*Sequoia sempervirens*
*Sequoiadendron giganteum*
*Thuja plicata*
*Tsuga heterophylla*
*Washingtonia filifera*
*Zauschneria californica*

Best in Part Shade

*Acer circinatum*
*Acer macrophyllum*
*Acer negundo var. californicum*
*Alnus oregona*
*Alnus rhombifolia*
*Calycanthus occidentalis*
*Carpenteria californica*
*Comarostaphylis diversifolia*
*Cornus nuttallii*
*Corylus cornuta var. californica*
*Equisetum hyemale*
*Garrya elliptica*
*Gaultheria shallon*
*Lithocarpus densiflora*
*Mahonia aquifolium*

*Mahonia nervosa*
*Physocarpus capitatus*
*Polystichum munitum*
*Rhododendron macrophyllum*
*Rhododendron occidentale*
*Ribes sanguineum*
*Ribes speciosum*
*Ribes viburnifolium*
*Rubus parviflorus*
*Sambucus caerulea*
*Satureja douglasii*
*Symphoricarpos albus*
*Vaccinium ovatum*
*Woodwardia fimbriata*

Tolerant to Considerable Shade

*Asarum caudatum*
*Equisetum hyemale*

*Gaultheria shallon*
*Lithocarpus densiflora*

Tolerant to Full Sun or Part Shade

*Aesculus californica*
*Arctostaphylos densiflora*

*Garrya elliptica*
*Gaultheria shallon*

235

Arctostaphylos edmundsii
Arctostaphylos hookeri
Arctostaphylos uva-ursi
Baccharis pilularis
Calocedrus decurrens
Calycanthus occidentalis
Carpenteria californica
Ceanothus gloriosus
Ceanothus griseus var. horizontalis
Ceanothus impressus
Ceanothus purpureus
Cercis occidentalis
Cercocarpus betuloides
   var. traskiae
Cercocarpus ledifolius
Chamaecyparis lawsoniana
Comarostaphylis diversifolia
Fragaria chiloensis
Dendromecon harfordii

Heteromeles arbutifolia
Holodiscus discolor
Mahonia aquifolium
Mahonia nervosa
Myrica californica
Pinus radiata
Prunus ilicifolia
Prunus lyonii
Pseudotsuga menziesii
Quercus agrifolia
Rhamnus californica
Rhamnus crocea
Rhus diversiloba
Rhus integrifolia
Sambucus caerulea
Thuja plicata
Umbellularia californica
Vaccinium ovatum

### Tolerant to Hot, Dry Situations

Adenostoma fasciculatum
Amelanchier alnifolia
Atriplex lentiformis var. breweri
Calocedrus decurrens
Cercocarpus betuloides
   var. traskiae
Cercocarpus ledifolius
Cercis occidentalis
Dendromecon harfordii
Eriogonum arborescens
Eriogonum fasciculatum
Eriogonum giganteum
Fremontodendron californicum
Fremontodendron mexicanum
Mahonia nevinii
Mahonia pinnata
Pinus coulteri

Pinus sabinana
Prunus ilicifolia
Prunus lyonii
Quercus chrysolepis
Quercus douglasii
Quercus kelloggii
Quercus lobata
Quercus wislizenii
Rhamnus crocea
Rhamnus californica
Rhus diversiloba
Rhus laurina
Rhus ovata
Romneya coulteri
Salvia leucophylla
Zauschneria californica

### Barrier Plants

Abies bracteata
Mahonia aquifolium
Mahonia nervosa
Mahonia nevinii

Mahonia pinnata
Prunus ilicifolia
Ribes speciosum

## Seacoast Conditions

*Aesculus californica*
*Arctostaphylos edmundsii*
*Arctostaphylos hookeri*
*Arctostaphylos uva-ursi*
*Artemisia pycnocephala*
*Atriplex lentiformis var. breweri*
*Baccharis pilularis*
*Ceanothus gloriosus*
*Ceanothus griseus var. horizontalis*
*Cupressus macrocarpa*
*Dendromecon harfordii*
*Eriogonum arborescens*
*Eriogonum fasciculatum*
*Eriogonum giganteum*

*Fragaria chiloensis*
*Fremontodendron californicum*
*Fremontodendron mexicanum*
*Galvezia speciosa*
*Garrya elliptica*
*Lyonothamnus floribundus*
*Myrica californica*
*Pinus contorta*
*Pinus muricata*
*Pinus radiata*
*Prunus ilicifolia*
*Prunus lyonii*
*Rhus integrifolia*
*Rhus ovata*

## Hedge and/or Screen

*Abies bracteata*
*Abies concolor*
*Abies magnifica*
*Acer circinatum*
*Adenostoma fasciculatum*
*Amelanchier alnifolia*
*Atriplex lentiformis var. breweri*
*Calocedrus decurrens*
*Calycanthus occidentalis*
*Carpenteria californica*
*Ceanothus impressus*
*Cercis occidentalis*
*Cercocarpus betuloides*
    *var. traskiae*
*Cercocarpus ledifolius*
*Chamaecyparis lawsoniana*
*Comarostaphylis diversifolia*
*Corylus cornuta var. californica*
*Dendromecon harfordii*
*Fremontodendron californicum*
*Fremontodendron mexicanum*
*Galvezia speciosa*
*Garrya elliptica*

*Heteromeles arbutifolia*
*Holodiscus discolor*
*Lyonothamnus floribundus*
*Mahonia aquifolium*
*Mahonia nevinii*
*Mahonia pinnata*
*Myrica californica*
*Physocarpus capitatus*
*Prunus ilicifolia*
*Prunus lyonii*
*Rhamnus californica*
*Rhamnus crocea*
*Rhododendron macrophyllum*
*Rhus integrifolia*
*Rhus laurina*
*Rhus ovata*
*Ribes sanguineum*
*Ribes speciosum*
*Sequoia sempervirens*
*Sequoiadendron giganteum*
*Thuja plicata*
*Tsuga heterophylla*

## Shade Trees

*Acer macrophyllum*
*Acer negundo var. californicum*

*Lyonothamnus floribundus*
    *var. asplenifolius*

*Alnus oregona*
*Alnus rhombifolia*
*Cupressus macrocarpa*
*Juglans hindsii*
*Lithocarpus densiflora*

*Platanus racemosa*
*Quercus agrifolia*
*Quercus lobata*
*Umbellularia californica*

Wind Tolerant

*Adenostoma fasciculatum*
*Aesculus californica*
*Artemisia pycnocephala*
*Atriplex lentiformis var. breweri*
*Arctostaphylos densiflora*
*Arctostaphylos edmundsii*
*Arctostaphylos hookeri*
*Arctostaphylos uva-ursi*
*Baccharis pilularis*
*Calocedrus decurrens*
*Ceanothus gloriosus*
*Ceanothus griseus var. horizontalis*
*Ceanothus impressus*
*Ceanothus purpureus*
*Cupressus macrocarpa*
*Eriogonum arborescens*
*Eriogonum fasciculatum*
*Eriogonum giganteum*

*Fragaria chiloensis*
*Garrya elliptica*
*Gaultheria shallon*
*Myrica californica*
*Prunus ilicifolia*
*Prunus lyonii*
*Rhamnus californica*
*Rhus ovata*
*Quercus agrifolia*
*Quercus chrysolepis*
*Quercus douglasii*
*Quercus kelloggii*
*Quercus lobata*
*Quercus wislizenii*
*Pinus radiata*
*Sambucus caerulea*
*Umbellularia californica*

Rapid Growing

*Acer macrophyllum*
*Acer negundo var. californicum*
*Alnus oregona*
*Alnus rhombifolia*
*Artemisia pycnocephala*
*Atriplex lentiformis var. breweri*
*Baccharis pilularis*
*Calycanthus occidentalis*
*Ceanothus impressus*
*Cercis occidentalis*
*Cercocarpus ledifolius*
*Cupressus macrocarpa*
*Equisetum hyemale*
*Eriogonum arborescens*
*Eriogonum fasciculatum*
*Eriogonum giganteum*

*Lyonothamnus floribundus*
*Mahonia nervosa*
*Pinus radiata*
*Pinus sabiniana*
*Platanus racemosa*
*Polystichum munitum*
*Prunus ilicifolia*
*Prunus lyonii*
*Pseudotsuga menziesii*
*Quercus lobata*
*Rhamnus californica*
*Rhododendron occidentale*
*Ribes sanguineum*
*Ribes viburnifolium*
*Salvia leucophylla*
*Satureja douglasii*

*Fragaria chiloensis*
*Fremontodendron californicum*
*Gaultheria shallon*
*Heteromeles arbutifolia*

*Sequoia sempervirens*
*Symphoricarpos albus*
*Tsuga heterophylla*
*Umbellularia californica*

### Erosion Control

*Aesculus californica*
*Atriplex lentiformis var. breweri*
*Baccharis pilularis*
*Cupressus macrocarpa*
*Eriogonum arborescens*
*Eriogonum fasciculatum*
*Eriogonum giganteum*
*Fragaria chiloensis*

*Fremontodendron californicum*
*Fremontodendron mexicanum*
*Heteromeles arbutifolia*
*Pinus radiata*
*Pinus sabiniana*
*Platanus racemosa*
*Romneya coulteri*

### Fall Colors

*Acer circinatum*
*Acer macrophyllum*
*Acer negundo var. californicum*
*Amelanchier alnifolia*

*Cercis occidentalis*
*Cornus nuttallii*
*Quercus kelloggii*
*Rhus diversiloba*

# BIBLIOGRAPHY

Baerg, Harry J. *How to Know the Western Trees.* Wm. C. Brown Co. Dubuque, Iowa. 1955

Bailey, L.H. *Cyclopaedia of Horticulture.* The MacMillan Co. New York, N.Y., 1928

Balls, Edward K. *Early Uses of California Plants.* U.C. Press, Berkeley, California 1962

Bowerman, Mary L. *The Flowering Plants and Ferns of Mount Diablo.* Gillick Press, Berkeley, California 1944

Ferris, Roxana. *Native Shrubs of the San Francisco Bay Region.* U.C. Press, Berkeley, California 1968

Grillos, Steve. *Ferns of California.* U.C. Press, Berkeley, California 1965

Holt, Vesta. *Keys for Identification of Wildflowers, Ferns, Trees, Shrubs and Woody Vines of Northern California.* National Press Publications, Palo Alto, California 1962

*Hortus Third.* MacMillan Co. New York, N.Y. 1977

Howell, John T. *Marin Flora.* U.C. Press, Berkeley, California 1949

Jepson, Willis. *Manual of the Flowering Plants of California.* U.C. Press, Berkeley, California 1925

Lenz, Lee. *Native Plants for California Gardens.* Rancho Santa Ana Botanical Garden, Claremont, California 1956

Maino and Howard. *Ornamental Trees.* U.C. Press, Berkeley, California 1955

McMinn, Howard. *An Illustrated Manual of California Shrubs.* U.C. Press, Berkeley, California 1939

McMinn, Howard and Maino, Evelyn. *An Illustrated Manual of Pacific Coast Trees.* U.C. Press, Berkeley, California 1959

Metcalf, Woodbridge. *Native Trees of the San Francisco Bay Region.* U.C. Press, Berkeley, California 1959

Munz, Philip. *California Desert Wildflowers.* U.C. Press, Berkeley, California 1962

Munz, Philip. *California Mountain Wildflowers.* U.C. Press, Berkeley, California 1963

Munz, Philip. *California Spring Wildflowers.* U.C. Press, Berkeley, California 1961

Munz, Philip. *Shore Wildflowers of California, Oregon and Washington.* U.C. Press, Berkeley, California 1964

Munz and Keck. *A California Flora.* U.C. Press, Berkeley, California 1973

Munz and Keck. *A Southern California Flora.* U.C. Press, Berkeley, California 1974

Peattie, Donald A. *A Natural History of Western Trees.* Haughton, Mifflin, Boston, Massachusetts 1953

Peterson and Peterson. *Native Trees of the Sierra Nevada.* U.C. Press, Berkeley, California 1975

Peterson, Victor. *Native Trees of Southern California.* U.C. Press, Berkeley, California 1968

Raven, Peter. *Native Shrubs of Southern California.* U.C. Press, Berkeley, California 1965

Rowntree, Lester. *Hardy Californians.* Peacock Press, Berkeley, California 1936

Rowntree, Lester. *Flowering Shrubs of California and Their Value to the Gardener.* Stanford University Press, Stanford, Palo Alto, California 1939

Sharsmith, Helen K. *Flora of the Mount Hamilton Range of California.* University Press, Notre Dame, Indiana 1945

Sudworth, George B. *Forest Trees of the Pacific Slope.* Dover Publications Inc. New York, N.Y. 1967

Sunset. *Western Garden Book.* Lane Publishing Co., Menlo Park, California.

Sweet, Muriel. *Common Edible and Useful Plants of the West.* Naturegraph, Healdsburg, California 1962

Thomas and Parnell. *Native Shrubs of the Sierra Nevada.* U.C. Press, Berkeley, California 1974

Watts, Tom. *A California Tree Finder.* Berkeley Nature Study. Berkeley, California 1963

# Glossary

*Acerose.*  Needle-like

*Achene.*  A small, dry, one-celled, one-seeded indehiscent fruit

*Acicular.*  See acerose

*Acuminate.*  Tapering to the apex, with the sides pinched in

*Acute.*  Tapering to the apex, with the sides about straight.

*Aggregate.*  A cluster of small fruit, developing from one flower

*Alternate.*  With one leaf at a node

*Annual.*  Life cycle completed in one season

*Apex.*  The tip

*Awl-shaped.*  Tapering to a point. Narrowly triangular

*Axillary.*  Borne in the axil of a leaf

*Berry.*  A fleshy, few- to many-seeded fruit, with immersed seed

*Biennial.*  Living for two years

*Bisexual.*  Having both stamens and pistils. Perfect

*Blade.*  The flat part of a leaf or petal

*Bloom.*  The whitish, powdery covering of a surface. Glaucous

*Bract.*  A small leaf-like structure near a flower or inflorescence

*Capsule.*  A dry fruit. Dehiscent, and usually with more than one seed

*Calyx.*  The outer portion of the flower. Sepals

*Catkin.*  A long, pendulous cluster of many small flowers. Either male or female

*Ciliate.*  With a marginal fringe of hairs

*Cleft.*  Cut in about one half way to the midvein or to the base

*Complete.*  A flower that has sepals, petals, stamens, pistils present

*Compound.*  Consisting of two or more distinct segments

*Cone.*  A dry, multiple fruit of a conifer. Consisting of over-lapping scales. Same as strobilus

*Cordate.*  Heart-shaped. Widest at the base

*Coriaceous.*  Leathery

*Corolla.*  Composed of the petals

*Corymb.*  A raceme-like inflorescence which is flat or convex at the top

*Crenate.*  With rounded teeth

*Crown.*  Used to mean either the top of a tree or the part of the trunk at the soil-line

*Cuneate.*  Wedge-shaped. Narrowest at the base

*Cuspidate.*  With a short, sharp, firm point

*Cyme.*  An inflorescence where the terminal flower blooms first

*Deciduous.*  Leaves all dying and falling off, usually in the winter period

*Decurrent.*  Extending downward from the point of insertion

*Dehiscent.*  Splitting open at maturity

*Deltoid.*  Triangular shape. Broadest at the base

*Dentate.*  Teeth are directed outward and are usually coarse

*Dimorphic.*  Comprised of two forms

*Dioecious.*  Male and female flowers on separate plants

*Dissected.*  Divided into numerous, usually narrow segments

*Divided.*  Deeply lobed. Nearly compound

*Drupe.*  A fleshy, indehiscent one-seeded fruit

*Elliptic.* Widest in the center, with the two ends equal
*Emarginate.* Shallowly notched at the apex
*Endemic.* Confined to a limited geographical area
*Entire.* Margins not toothed
*Evergreen.* With green leaves all year long
*Exotic.* Not native. Introduced
*Exfoliating.* Peeling off in thin layers

*Falcate.* Asymmetric. Curved sideways. Tapering to apex
*Fascicled.* In close clusters or bundles
*Frond.* Leaf of a fern

*Glabrous.* With no hairs
*Glaucous.* Covered with a whitish or grayish or bluish waxy bloom
*Globose.* Round as a globe

*Hastate.* Arrow-shaped, with basal lobes pointing outward
*Head.* A compact flower cluster in which lateral flowers bloom first
*Herbaceous.* With no persistent woody stem above ground
*Hybrid.* A cross between two related species

*Indehiscent.* Not splitting open
*Indigenous.* Native to an area
*Inflorescence.* Arrangement of flowers on a stem
*Involute.* With margins rolled upward
*Irregular.* Not symmetrical

*Lanceolate.* Lance-shaped. Widest below the middle
*Leaflet.* A division of a compound leaf
*Legume.* A pod. The fruit of a member of the Leguminosae family
*Linear.* Long and narrow with parallel sides
*Lobe.* A division of a leaf, especially if rounded

*Midrib.* Main or central vein of a leaf
*Monoecious.* Male and female flowers on the same plant
*Mucronate.* With a small, tooth-like apex. Not expecially sharp

*Nerve.* A simple or unbranched vein
*Node.* Place on a stem where a leaf is attached
*Nut.* A dry, hard, one-celled, indehiscent fruit

*Obcordate.* Inversely cordate
*Oblanceolate.* Inversely lanceolate
*Oblique.* With sides unequal, especially at the base
*Oblong.* With parallel sides and two to four times longer than wide
*Obovate.* Inversely ovate
*Obovoid.* Inversely ovoid
*Obtuse.* Blunt to rounded at the apex
*Opposite.* With two leaves at a node
*Orbicular.* Circular. A leaf that is round
*Ovate.* Egg-shaped. Widest at the base. An ovate leaf
*Ovoid.* Egg-shaped. As an egg

*Palmately compound.* With all the leaflets borne at the top of the petiole
*Panicle.* A compound flower cluster with the younger flowers at the center
*Parted.* Lobed, or cut in over half-way to base of mid-rib
*Pedicel.* Stalk of a single flower of an inflorescence
*Peduncle.* Stalk of a simple flower or of an inflorescence
*Peltate.* With the petiole attached to the leaf blade in from the margin
*Pendulous.* Weeping. Hanging down
*Perennial.* Living for three or more years
*Petiole.* Stalk to a leaf blade or to a compound leaf
*Phyllode.* Flattened petiole which performs the functions of a leaf blade
*Pinna.* One of the primary divisions of a pinnately compound leaf
*Pinnately compound.* With the leaflets on opposite sides of an axis
*Pistillate.* Female. Comprised of pistils
*Pod.* Legume. A dry, dehiscent fruit. Of the Leguminosae family
*Pubescent.* With short, soft hairs

*Raceme.* A compound flower cluster with the flower stems of equal length and with
the younger flowers nearest the apex
*Regular.* Radially symmetrical
*Reniform.* Kidney-shaped
*Reticulate.* In the form of a network
*Revolute.* Rolled back from the margins
*Rhizome.* A horizontal, underground stem
*Rhombic.* Diamond-shaped. Opposite sides parallel

*Samara.* A dry, indehiscent, winged fruit
*Sagittate.* Arrow-shaped, with the basal lobes directed backward
*Scabrous.* Rough to the touch
*Serrate.* With the sharp teeth directed forward
*Sessile.* Without a stalk
*Simple.* Consisting of one part
*Spatulate.* Spoon-shaped. Broad and rounded at the apex
*Spike.* A compound flower cluster with sessile flowers on an elongated axis, and
with the younger flowers at the apex
*Staminate.* Male. With stamens
*Stellate.* Star-shaped, star-like
*Stipule.* An appendage at the base of the petiole or leaf
*Stolon.* A horizontal, above-ground stem
*Stomata.* Small openings in the leaf surface

*Tomentose.* With hairs closely interwoven
*Truncate.* Squared at the apex or the base

*Umbel.* A compound flower cluster with the flowers all from one point and with
the younger flowers in the center
*Undulated.* With a wavy margin

*Valve.* One of the parts into which a dehiscent fruit splits
*Viscid.* Sticky

*Whorled.* With three or more parts from one point

# Index

# APPENDIX

## Places Where Native Plants
## Might Be Seen

Arboretums
Botanic Gardens
Cemeteries
College Campuses
Golf Courses
Forested Areas
    Federal
    Private
    State

Parks
    City
    County
    National
    Regional
    State
School Grounds and
    other open areas

Commercial sources of California native plants and seed are sometimes listed by and available to members of various organizations, including the California Native Plant Society, Suite D, 2380 Ellsworth Street, Berkeley, California 94704.